WESTWARD MOVEMENT

BUFFALO BILL, *Stevenson*
DANIEL BOONE, *Stevenson*
DAVY CROCKETT, *Parks*
JESSIE FREMONT, *Wagoner*
JED SMITH, *Burt*
JIM BOWIE, *Winders*
JIM BRIDGER, *Winders*
KIT CARSON, *Stevenson*
LOTTA CRABTREE, *Place*
MERIWETHER LEWIS, *Bebenroth*
NARCISSA WHITMAN, *Warner*
SACAGAWEA, *Seymour*
SAM HOUSTON, *Stevenson*
TECUMSEH, *Stevenson*
WILL CLARK, *Wilkie*
WILLIAM HENRY HARRISON,
  Peckham
ZEB PIKE, *Stevenson*

THE NATION DIVIDED

ABE LINCOLN, *Stevenson*
BEDFORD FORREST, *Parks*
CLARA BARTON, *Stevenson*
DAVID FARRAGUT, *Long*
HARRIET BEECHER STOWE,
  Widdemer
JEB STUART, *Winders*
JULIA WARD HOWE, *Wagoner*
MARY TODD LINCOLN, *Wilkie*
RAPHAEL SEMMES, *Snow*
ROBERT E. LEE, *Monsell*
TOM JACKSON, *Monsell*
U. S. GRANT, *Stevenson*

RECONSTRUCTION and EXPANSION

ALECK BELL, *Widdemer*
BOOKER T. WASHINGTON,
  Stevenson
JOHN WANAMAKER, *Burt*

LOUISA ALCOTT, *Wagoner*
LUTHER BURBANK, *Burt*
MARIA MITCHELL, *Melin*
MARK TWAIN, *Mason*
MARY MAPES DODGE, *Mason*
SITTING BULL, *Stevenson*
SUSAN ANTHONY, *Monsell*
TOM EDISON, *Guthridge*

TURN of the CENTURY

ANNIE OAKLEY, *Wilson*
DAN BEARD, *Mason*
GEORGE CARVER, *Stevenson*
GEORGE DEWEY, *Long*
GEORGE EASTMAN, *Henry*
JAMES WHITCOMB RILEY, *Mitche*
JANE ADDAMS, *Wagoner*
JOHN PHILIP SOUSA, *Weil*
JULIETTE LOW, *Higgins*
KATE DOUGLAS WIGGIN, *Mason*
THE RINGLING BROTHERS, *Burt*
ROBERT PEARY, *Clark*
TEDDY ROOSEVELT, *Parks*
WALTER REED, *Higgins*
WILBUR AND ORVILLE WRIGHT,
  Stevenson
WILL AND CHARLIE MAYO,
  Hammontree

IN RECENT YEARS

AMELIA EARHART, *Howe*
A. P. GIANNINI, *Hammontree*
BABE RUTH, *Van Riper*
ERNIE PYLE, *Wilson*
FRANKLIN ROOSEVELT, *Weil*
HENRY FORD, *Aird-Ruddiman*
JIM THORPE, *Van Riper*
KNUTE ROCKNE, *Van Riper*
LOU GEHRIG, *Van Riper*
RICHARD BYRD, *Van Riper*
WILL ROGERS, *Van Riper*
WOODROW WILSON, *Monsell*

Cyrus McCormick

Farmer Boy

Illustrated by John Nielsen

Cyrus McCormick

Farmer Boy

by Lavinia Dobler

THE **BOBBS-MERRILL** COMPANY, INC.
A SUBSIDIARY OF HOWARD W. SAMS & CO., INC.
Publishers · INDIANAPOLIS · NEW YORK

For my aunt
Clara Dobler Christman

Illustrations

Numerous smaller illustrations

Contents

CHILDHOOD
★ ★ ★ ★
OF FAMOUS
★ ★ ★
AMERICANS

★   ★   ★

★ # Cyrus
McCormick

Farmer Boy

A Virginia
Plantation

YOUNG CYRUS pushed through the bushes to the walnut tree. When he reached the big tree, he was disappointed. It was not the one he and Jo had marked a few months ago with a *C* and the year, *1814.*

Cyrus McCormick remembered that day. It had been his birthday, February 15, and he had been five years old. He had used his grandfather's knife to carve the letter and numbers on the trunk of the old tree.

Now he walked quickly over to another large tree in the Virginia woods. This one did not have a mark on the trunk, either. Cyrus was puzzled. Everything seemed strange and different. Maybe he really had lost his way.

The fish net he had slung over his shoulder was getting heavier with every step he took. The net was dragging on the ground behind him. Cyrus knew now that bringing it had not been a good idea.

Cyrus was in the woods this May morning to catch a fox with the big net. He had searched under the bushes and behind the trees. He was disappointed that he had not seen a fox, not even the tip of a red tail.

He stared at the dark trees. They looked like giants. They made him feel small and lonely.

"I'm not afraid. I'm a big boy," he said to the trees. He threw back his shoulders. Cyrus hoped the sound of his voice would give him more confidence.

He heard a faint answer, "Big boy."

It didn't make him feel big or brave at all.

For a minute he thought someone mocking him was hiding behind one of those large trees.

"That's my echo," he said to himself, shrugging his shoulders.

Cyrus stumbled on, still searching for the tree that was carved with the letter *C*. He was quite certain he was on the land his father owned behind their home, Walnut Grove Plantation, in Rockridge County, Virginia.

"I wonder if any of my uncles in Ireland or Scotland ever got lost," he said. "Uncle William is a brave American. He had to be to fight in the War of 1812."

Cyrus leaned against a sturdy oak. He could not see the sun because of the many green leaves on the trees. He had no idea how far he was from home, and he did not know which way to walk. Now he was sure he was lost.

"I should have brought Papa's compass," he said aloud.

Cyrus was barefooted, and his feet hurt. It had started to rain, and the ground was muddy. It would be harder than ever now to catch a fox. He was really disappointed that he had not seen at least one fox.

Red foxes and wolves had stolen chickens and lambs from his father and other farmers in the Valley of Virginia. When the farmers offered to give a reward for every fox and wolf that was caught, Cyrus had made up his mind to try to catch one.

As the rain splattered his face and the wind whistled, Cyrus wished he had told Jo about his plan to get the reward. Still, he had purposely gone into the forest without taking Jo with him. He had wanted to prove that he could catch a fox without Jo's help.

He had found out, though, that it wasn't fun being in the dark woods alone. He wished Jo was with him. Jo was two years older than

Cyrus. Maybe if he had come, they might have found a fox. Jo had sharp black eyes.

"Cyrus! Cyrus McCormick!" It was Jo Anderson, Cyrus's Negro playmate, calling.

"Jo!" Cyrus called back eagerly. Now his voice was loud and strong. He wasn't afraid any more. As long as Cyrus could remember, Jo had been watching over him.

"Where are you?" Jo called.

"You-u-u," came an echo.

"In the woods," Cyrus answered.

"Woods," said the echo.

"I'm coming," Jo yelled.

Bushes rustled and Jo ran toward Cyrus. "Are you all right?" Jo asked.

"Yes," Cyrus nodded, "but I'm glad you're here."

"Why did you come to the woods without me?" Jo said to Cyrus. "I have been looking for you all over the plantation."

"I wanted to catch a fox," Cyrus answered. "Maybe two foxes."

"Pappy will lick me good if he finds out you went off without me," Jo said. "He told me to stay with you all the time. Please don't do it again," Jo begged.

"I won't," Cyrus said, and he meant it, "but I wanted to see if I could catch a fox by myself."

"How are you going to catch a fox?" Jo asked.

"With Grandpa's old fish net," Cyrus explained. "If I can find a fox asleep in the woods, I can catch it."

"A fox is smart," Jo said. "He is quick, too. That's why your papa sets traps for foxes and wolves." He burst out laughing, and his black eyes were bright. "I saw Mister Robert unlock the door of the blacksmith shop just now."

"You did?" Cyrus was excited. "Maybe he is going to work on the reaper. Let's hurry!"

The boys, heading toward Walnut Grove

Plantation, carried the net between them. As the boys ran back to the plantation, the rain came down fast and whipped their homespun clothes.

"Maybe Papa is working on something new," Cyrus said, "but I hope it's the reaper."

The boys were now only a few feet away from the blacksmith shop. It was a sturdy building of stone and wood that stood against the side of the hill near the mill and the barn.

"The farmers need Papa's machine," Cyrus said proudly. "I don't like to have them work so hard. Even my back hurts when I watch the men cut the ripe wheat."

"It's hard work using a sickle," Jo agreed. "I can't keep up with Mister Robert's ideas," he added thoughtfully.

"Neither can I," Cyrus said. "He has so many. I wish he could work on them all the time."

"He has a big place here," Jo said. "There are the kilns and many other things he has to do."

17

"Before we get to the shop," Cyrus said, "we'll put Grandpa McCormick's net in the barn."

"Of course, we should put it back where you found it," Jo nodded.

"I can hardly wait to see what Papa is doing," Cyrus said, as they hurried toward the barn.

The boys hung the net on a long hook and then ran from the barn to the blacksmith shop.

They opened the heavy walnut door and shut it quickly to keep out the wind and rain. The hard dirt floor was covered with wood shavings and bits of metal and leather. The bright fire burning on the brick hearth lighted the large workroom.

"Papa," Cyrus called eagerly. His words were drowned by the pounding of the rain on the slanted roof. "I guess he didn't hear us," Cyrus said to Jo. "Let's dry our clothes before we talk to him."

Both boys backed as close to the fire as they

19

could, so they would get dry as quickly as possible. While waiting, Cyrus looked at the sickles, knives, horseshoes, and tongs that hung from the walls and ceiling or lay scattered about on the benches.

The blacksmith shop was his favorite spot on the big plantation. Cyrus would have gone there more often, but his father often kept it locked. Sometimes Cyrus was permitted to help him. Cyrus was very impatient for the time when he would be old enough to shoe a horse or repair some tools by himself.

"Papa," Cyrus called again, now that his clothes were almost dry. He walked over to the forge where Mr. McCormick was working. Jo followed.

His father looked up as he heard his son's voice. "When did you get here?" he asked, surprised. Mr. McCormick pushed his dark brown hair off his forehead, and his muscles rippled.

"A few minutes ago," Cyrus answered, looking at the iron rod his father held in his hand.

"What are you making?" Cyrus asked. It didn't look like something for a reaper.

"A crane for cooking," his father said. "This will hold an iron pot. It should make your mother's work in the kitchen easier."

"Oh," Cyrus said. He was disappointed. "I had hoped it was some new part for the reaper."

Cyrus had faith in the farm machine, but his father did not work on the reaper as often as Cyrus wanted him to do so.

"Maybe this winter, when I don't have to be in the fields," Mr. McCormick said, "I can find some time to work on it."

"The farmers need that reaper you've been working on," Cyrus said earnestly.

Mr. McCormick laughed. "Seems to me, son, you're mighty young to be so interested in this unfinished reaper."

"I want to see that machine cut wheat," Cyrus said, determination in his voice.

"Here, you and Jo get more wood," his father suggested, changing the subject. "I need a hot fire to get this crane shaped with a hook."

"I'd rather help you work on the new machine," Cyrus said, but he and Jo went over to the corner and brought back a big log.

"Your mother thinks the reaper is a wild idea," Mr. McCormick continued. "It means experimenting, and so far I haven't been able to make it work. But I seem to make other useful things."

Cyrus and his father worked together as Jo watched them. Mr. McCormick stopped suddenly and looked at his oldest son.

"Cyrus, maybe you'll be the one who will invent a reaper that will really work and will help the farmers."

The boy's eyes were bright as he smiled at his father's words.

22

A Gift to Remember

CYRUS TURNED the knob on the heavy pine door, and Cyrus and Jo walked into the kitchen. They had been in the orchard gathering red apples that had dropped from the gnarled trees.

"Where's Mama?" Cyrus asked Eunice, as he put the heavy pail of fruit on a bench by the stone fireplace. Almost all of the cooking was done at this stone fireplace.

"She and Mister Robert left about an hour ago for your grandparent's home," Eunice said, as she peeled a big potato. Eunice was Jo's mother and the family's cook.

"They got word that your Uncle William Hall

has yellow fever, and the old folks are ill, too." Eunice sighed and looked at the five-year-old boy. "I sure hope no one on this plantation gets that awful yellow fever."

"We don't want to get sick, do we Jo?" Cyrus asked his playmate.

When Cyrus got sick, it meant he could not go to the blacksmith shop.

"No, sir," Jo said, shaking his curly head, and his black eyes opened wide.

"I sure hope Uncle William will be well soon," Cyrus said.

This uncle was the boy's favorite relative. Cyrus was proud that his Uncle William had fought bravely in the War of 1812. A couple of days before, he had returned to Virginia because he was ill with a fever that turned his body yellow. Cyrus knew how worried his mother was, and now his grandparents were ill, too.

Susan, the baby, started to cry and Cyrus went

over to rock the cradle. He talked softly to her as he sat down on the stool near the fireplace. Cyrus saw that his brother Robert was asleep in the trundle bed in the corner. Cyrus yawned and in a few minutes he had fallen asleep, too.

Later Eunice called, "Supper! Supper is ready. Time to eat."

Cyrus woke up with a start and almost fell off the stool. He blinked his eyes and said, "I'm not hungry, Eunice. I don't want any supper."

"You miss your mama," Eunice said kindly as she put her dark hand on his hot forehead. "Drink some of this fresh milk, and then I'll help you get ready for bed."

The next thing Cyrus knew was that his body seemed to be on fire. He opened his eyes, and to his surprise he found that he was sitting in a tub of steaming hot water. A white sheet like a tent was around the wooden tub.

Cyrus turned his wet head and saw his father.

Mr. McCormick was sitting near him on a three-legged stool. He held onto his son so that he wouldn't slip.

The dark-haired man smiled at the sick boy. "You are feeling much better, aren't you, Son?" he asked gently.

Cyrus rubbed his eyes. "I guess so," he said slowly and quietly.

"I'm going to lift you out of this tub and get you dry as soon as I can," his father explained. "We don't want you to catch cold."

Cyrus dried his face and chest with the white linen towel and his father rubbed his back. It felt so good. Then Mr. McCormick wrapped him in a woolen blanket and carried his son to the big bed.

"Have I been sick?" Cyrus asked as his head sank down on the soft pillow.

"You've had yellow fever, but you will be well in no time," Mr. McCormick said confidently.

"I wouldn't let the doctor bleed you, Son. We've already lost your Grandfather and Grandmother Hall, as well as several of our good neighbors."

Mrs. McCormick came into the room, holding a cup in her hand. "Drink this hot tea, Cyrus," she said. "It will give you strength."

She put the cup on the table and helped Cyrus raise up on the pillow so that he could drink the tea more easily.

Cyrus sipped the steaming tea. It tasted bitter. "I don't like it," he said, shaking his head.

"You've been mighty sick," his mother said. "I'll put some honey in to sweeten the tea."

As Cyrus drank slowly, his mother turned to her husband. "Robert, those hot steam baths made of herbs have helped Cyrus. I am grateful that you insisted we try them."

"The doctors are learning more all the time about the ailments we humans have," Mr. Mc-Cormick said. "It seems natural to me that a person who is sick should be given a tonic to build him up."

"There are healing herbs in that hot tea, Cyrus," his mother told him. "It may taste bitter but it is good for you. You'll be up and running around the farm in no time."

"I hope so," Cyrus said in a weak voice, as he lay quietly in bed. He just wanted to sleep.

"I hope when you are a grown man, Son," his father said, "people will know a lot more than they do now to prevent sickness." He paused. "If you ever have people working for you, it will be your responsibility to provide ways to help them remain strong and well."

Cyrus was never to forget that siege with yellow fever. All through his life he tried to take good care of his body, by resting and exercising and eating the right foods. He also encouraged the people who worked for him to take care of their health.

28

Soon Cyrus was well again, and interested in everything that was happening around Walnut Grove Plantation.

While he was recovering, Cyrus and his father planned that Cyrus should learn to ride as soon as he was able. The important day for riding a horse had come at last.

"Papa, I want to be a good rider like you," Cyrus said, as Mr. McCormick lifted him up on the light reddish-brown horse.

"Hold on tight to the saddle horn," his father warned him.

Cyrus held on tightly. Mr. McCormick led the horse with the four white legs along the tree-shaded road.

The boy sat up straight and tall in the saddle. "I want to ride all by myself," Cyrus insisted. "I would like a horse just like this one. He is gentle." Cyrus patted the sorrel's neck. "He wouldn't run away with me."

"No, I don't think he would," his father answered. "You will have to have many lessons before you are a good enough rider to have your own horse."

Cyrus tightened his grip on the horn, but he didn't say anything. He was sure that it wouldn't be too long before he would have his own horse.

Mr. McCormick looked back. "You are doing all right." He smiled. "One of these days, Son, we'll get a saddle that fits you. I can't make the stirrups of this saddle short enough for your short legs."

"I'm a big boy," Cyrus said. "My legs aren't very short."

"They are long for a boy your age," Mr. McCormick assured him. "Only this saddle was made for a great big man."

That made Cyrus feel better, but he wished he could grow up real fast. He wanted to be as tall and as strong as his father.

30

"This horse likes you," Mr. McCormick said, as the graceful animal walked carefully along the road.

"I like him." Cyrus again patted the horse's long brown neck.

"Yes, he's a fine animal," replied Mr. Mc-Cormick, as he led the horse and the young rider back into the yard. "Now, Cyrus, I'll help you get off. You may take the horse back to Jo to unsaddle. Be careful that you do not frighten the peacocks."

Two peacocks strutted on the green velvet grass nearby. Their royal blue and gold feathers sparkled in the sun. Mrs. McCormick took pride in these beautiful birds, and Cyrus often helped her scatter corn on the lawn for them to eat.

"Mama's peacocks are about the prettiest birds we have on our farm," Cyrus said, admiring them.

"Your mother would be pleased that you think

so," Mr. McCormick said. "She is mighty proud of her peacocks."

"I've already told her that I think they are beautiful," Cyrus said.

"Good for you!" His father smiled. "Did you know that many kings in Europe have peacocks? Some people call them the birds of royalty."

"Mother likes them because they are handsome and proud," Cyrus answered.

Cyrus carefully led the horse away. Mr. McCormick went on to his work. The first riding lesson was over.

In a very short time Cyrus was riding very well. Cyrus begged many times to go with his father when he made the rounds of the plantation. Mr. McCormick finally decided that he should have a horse of his own.

Mr. McCormick had observed that Cyrus was not afraid of horses and that he made many excuses to be around them. Cyrus would talk to the horses. Since he was not tall enough to pet them, he begged his father to pick him up so that he could touch their long, soft noses.

One day Mr. McCormick walked into the barn to find Cyrus standing in front of the stall talking to the white-footed sorrel.

"Someday I hope I have a horse just like you

for my own," Mr. McCormick heard Cyrus tell the horse. "Then we will ride all over Walnut Grove. But I want a horse with four white feet."

"Hello, Son," Mr. McCormick called out as he walked over to the stall. "So you like this sorrel."

"Papa, you know I do," Cyrus answered.

A few weeks later Jo and Cyrus were walking toward the barn when Cyrus stopped suddenly. Standing near his father and a neighbor was a light brown horse with four white legs.

"Isn't he handsome?" the boy said enthusiastically. "He looks a little bit like the one Papa lets me ride, but I know he isn't. He holds his head so high and he seems so proud."

"He looks like a fine horse," Jo said.

"I wonder what Papa and that man are talking about," Cyrus said, walking faster. Jo had to run to keep up with him.

As Cyrus came closer, the horse whinnied and pulled on the rope.

"You are beautiful," Cyrus said to the horse. Then he turned to his father, "Papa, whose horse is this beauty?" 1747131

Mr. McCormick smiled. "Yours, Son."

"Mine?" Cyrus was almost speechless. He had really not thought he would be this fortunate.

"I'm the luckiest boy in Virginia," Cyrus said. "I bet he can strut."

"He is the best horse I've had in years," the farmer replied.

"Papa, when can I ride him?" Cyrus asked.

"As soon as you saddle him," Mr. McCormick answered.

"Come on, Jo, help me get the saddle," Cyrus yelled as he ran as fast as he could to the barn.

Later, as they rode along the road together, Mr. McCormick said, "Son, you have the makings of a good horseman. Treat your horse as your good friend, and he will trust you. We should be kind to animals."

35

"I'll always be kind to my horse," Cyrus said confidently.

His father went on. "Men who are good to their horses are usually considerate of the people with whom they work. You will have a fuller life, if you think of other people."

Cyrus had never been quite so happy as he rode the horse that now belonged to him.

"Papa, my horse is proud. Look at the way he holds his head," Cyrus said. "See how he struts!"

"This sorrel has a proud way with him," his father said, watching his son ride.

"I'm going to call him Peacock," Cyrus announced suddenly. "He struts just like Mother's beautiful peacocks."

Father's Machine

BEFORE CYRUS was up that Saturday morning, Mr. McCormick was already in the shop working on the reaper.

More than anything else, Cyrus wanted to help his father with the machine.

He opened the door of the shop and walked over to where his father was working. Cyrus started to ask a question, but Mr. McCormick said sharply, "Son, don't bother me. I think I have figured out a new way to make this reaper work, but I don't want you here today."

Cyrus turned around and walked slowly toward the thick walnut door.

37

Jo was waiting outside. "Let's get our chores done in a hurry. Then let's go fishing."

"All right." Cyrus sighed, but he was not too enthusiastic. He liked working with tools. He was happy when he was in the shop. Surely there was something he could do to help his father with the reaper. However, he had just been told that his father did not want him.

"When your Papa needs you, he will call you," Jo assured him. "Anyway, it's cooler by the water than in the hot blacksmith shop."

Jo ran to the barn to get the fishing poles. He also picked up the clay mug that held the wiggly angleworms. Jo had dug them earlier that summer morning in the garden.

The boys stood on the bank. Their poles dangled in the water. Jo spoke softly, "When your Papa has worked out whatever's bothering him, he'll be in a better mood. Then I'm sure he'll need you."

Before Cyrus could answer, he felt a big tug on his line. He pulled hard. "I think I have a fish," he shouted.

Cyrus had to hold on tight as he drew the squirming fish out of the water. "Gee, it's a big one!" Cyrus exclaimed.

"That's a good catch," Jo said. "I hope I'm as lucky as you."

"You may catch a bigger one," Cyrus said.

"I have a nibble," Jo yelled.

"Hang on tight," Cyrus warned. He had forgotten about his father's machine.

"Maybe if our luck keeps up, we'll get enough fish for supper tonight," Cyrus said as he put another earthworm on his hook. "At least I can please Mother, and another day maybe I can please Papa."

The boys fished silently. Soon they had a big catch to take home. Jo and Cyrus helped Eunice clean the fish for the supper.

Mr. McCormick wasn't at supper with the family that night. He worked in his shop long after the children had gone to bed.

The wheat had grown fast that summer of 1816. The morning after the fish dinner, seven-year-old Cyrus and Jo stood on one of the low rolling hills and watched the wheat waving in the wind against the dull gray sky.

"It looks like a lot of wheat to harvest," Jo said.

"Yes, and a lot of hard work for all of us, even Mother," Cyrus said glumly. Then his face lighted up. "Papa's machine will come in handy this year."

"It isn't ready, is it?" Jo asked, shaking his head sadly.

"It may be by harvest time," Cyrus said hopefully. "I wish we didn't always have so much rain around here."

Later that day, when Cyrus quietly opened the door of the shop, he saw his father hovering over the wooden machine. The floor creaked, and Mr. McCormick looked up.

Cyrus walked over to the reaper. "Is it almost finished?" he asked eagerly.

"Almost." His father nodded. Cyrus saw a sparkle in his brown eyes. "I have to check to be sure the sickles are on tight," Mr. McCormick said. "We'll try it out tomorrow, rain or shine."

If the machine could cut wheat in the rain, then it would be a success. Cyrus thought of how hard it was with the hand sickle when the stalks of grain were wet. He surely hoped it wouldn't rain tomorrow.

When Cyrus woke up the next morning, he ran to the window. The clouds were low in the sky and everything he touched was damp. This was not a good day to test the reaper.

Cyrus and Jo hurried through their chores and then headed for the shop.

The odd-looking machine had already been

moved from the blacksmith shop to a level spot on hard ground. Cyrus checked the six shining sickles that were bolted to the wooden bar. They seemed to be working fine. Behind the bar was a platform that held six wooden cylinders with spikes, each a foot and a half high, which turned when the cylinders moved.

Cyrus took a deep breath. The machine looked wonderful to him. He studied the dark sky. He wished the sun was shining. He wiggled his toes. His feet were damp from the wet grass.

Old Charlie, Jo's father, hitched the horses, Dolly and Dick, behind the reaper. Cyrus thought that looked peculiar. Then he remembered that his father had told him that a horse would push the machine, not pull it, so that the grain would not be trampled.

"The cutting will be done in front of the reaper," his father explained.

Cyrus noticed the stout whippletrees. Those

swinging bars, connected with a heavy tongue, stood out in back of the reaper. The two horses were hitched there so that they could push the machine. However, the horses were nervous. They did not seem to know what they were supposed to do. They were used to pulling wagons, not pushing something as strange as this reaper.

"They are smart horses," Grandfather McCormick said sympathetically. "Dolly and Dick will get the idea after a few tries."

Cyrus looked at his grandfather. Grandfather had many problems, but he was always calm. He, too, hoped that the machine would work today.

After several attempts, with old Charlie patiently encouraging the horses, the machine moved a few feet. Wherever the path was smooth, it was much easier, but the reaper was hard to manage on uneven or rocky land. Once Cyrus thought it was going to turn over.

At last, the horses pulled the machine into the

wheat field. It wasn't raining now, but the grain stalks were so drenched that they leaned against each other for support.

"We're ready to cut the wheat!" Mr. McCormick shouted. He was nervous and his voice was high.

The cylinders went round and round. The spikes turned. The knives were in place. But the wheat lay so limp that the reaper slid right over the stalks, not cutting them. The horses trampled the grain behind the reaper.

No one said a word. Cyrus looked at his grandfather, but he didn't seem too disappointed. Mrs. McCormick was nearby with Robert, Hannah, and Eunice. Jo was standing by Cyrus.

"I think I'll set those spikes so they will be lower," Mr. McCormick said as he bent down to adjust them.

In a few minutes he stood up. Cyrus was proud of how straight and tall he was.

"We're ready to test the machine again," Mr. McCormick said, after he was satisfied that the spikes were the way he wanted them.

The reaper cut a few stalks, but not more than an armful. The machine slipped over the wet wheat in the level places of the field and stuck when the ground was uneven.

Mr. McCormick wiped his forehead. "It won't work!" He sighed.

Cyrus's mother stepped forward. She looked directly at her husband. "Isn't the wheat too wet?" she asked. "I'm sure the machine would work if the wheat were only dry and straight."

"You know we generally have rain when we're ready to harvest," Mr. McCormick said. "If my machine can't cut wet wheat, then it is no good to the farmers!"

"The other inventions you have worked on have been successful," Mrs. McCormick said. "I don't know what I would do without the crane for cooking that you made for me. What about the bellows in the shop and the machine for water power?" she asked.

"They aren't complicated," Mr. McCormick answered slowly, "but this reaper is. It's no use to try to make this machine cut grain."

Grandfather McCormick walked over to his son. "Robert, you are on the right track. You'll have to work on it some more."

"Well, maybe, but I doubt that I will," Mr. McCormick answered.

He turned around. "Charlie, bring the cradles," he called. "We're late now. The wheat will be too ripe if we waste any more precious time."

Cyrus knew only too well how all those present dreaded swinging the heavy grain cradles. Those big scythes had curved wooden arms set on a handle to hold the grain upright as the wheat was cut. Then they were swung to the side.

Cyrus turned to Jo. "Papa needs us more than

ever before," he said. "We can rake, while the men cut the grain."

"We're good rakers," Jo told him. "I'm all ready to start."

As the boys raked the ripe buds, Cyrus looked out over the field. He stopped to rest.

"Jo," he said, "I think there is a way to make a reaper that *will* cut wet grain."

The Bad Trade

Cyrus sat on the hard bench in the classroom of the Field School. He was trying to study his lesson, but he was not able to pay attention. He kept looking toward the desk where the teacher sat, correcting the students' spelling.

Cyrus hoped he had not misspelled any of those words, but some of them were tricky. He whispered the jingle:

"*I* before *e*,
Except after *c*,
Or when sounded like *a*
As in neighbor or weigh."

He heaved a sigh. At least he was sure that those *ie* words, *believe* and *grieve,* were correct.

Cyrus was startled when he heard the instructor's voice. "Master McCormick, come to my desk."

He rose slowly from the bench. What did the teacher want? This thin man with the long, sharp nose was very strict, and he used the switch freely—too freely.

Cyrus could not tell from the tone in the instructor's voice whether he was pleased or annoyed.

As Cyrus walked slowly to the front of the bare classroom, all he could see was the big switch that lay across the desk. Cyrus felt the eyes of the other students on him.

"Here is your slate with the spelling words," the schoolmaster said.

Cyrus took the slate and glanced at the board. There were no checks on it. That meant that he had not misspelled any words.

The schoolmaster stood up. "Class," he said

in a severe voice. "This is the third week in a row that Master McCormick has had a perfect spelling score. He is the only one with that record. You students should study as hard as he does and should try for the kind of record he has made in this class."

The teacher now turned to Cyrus. "Young man," he said, "you not only have a good memory, but you apply yourself. You will be successful when you are older."

"Thank you, sir," Cyrus said. He was embarrassed to be praised in front of all the students. He walked back to the bench with his slate, his head down.

The boy next to him made a face and whispered, "Teacher's pet."

Cyrus did not dare answer back. If the schoolmaster heard them talking, they would both be punished. Cyrus had no desire to have to stay late after school or be switched.

51

Cyrus was sure of one thing. He was *not* the teacher's pet. Cyrus would have to settle that very soon with Percy.

When the teacher dismissed the class for the day, Cyrus caught up with Percy and the other boys walking along.

"Percy, I am *not* a teacher's pet, and you know it," Cyrus said, touching the boy's shirt.

"Let go of me," Percy squirmed, hunching his shoulders.

"Why did you call me the teacher's pet?" Cyrus asked.

"Because you are the teacher's pet," Percy said defensively. "Do you want to fight?" he asked, clenching his fists.

"Of course not," Cyrus said, but he was angry. "No one ever proves anything by fighting. Just because I spelled all the words right is no reason for you to call me what you did."

"What difference does it make? I don't care

whether a word is spelled right or not," Percy said. "You can still read it."

"It makes a big difference," Cyrus argued. He looked straight at Percy. "How would you like to have your name spelled this way?" Cyrus smoothed off some dirt with his big toe. Then he bent down, wrote Percy's name with his index finger, and spelled Percy with an *i* instead of a *y*.

"That's not the way to spell my name." Percy was indignant.

"I know it isn't," Cyrus agreed. "You like to have your name spelled correctly, too. Some people who are careless spellers wouldn't bother."

"Those people are not *my* friends," Percy said. Then he broke into a smile. "Spelling is more important than I realized. Guess I'd better study harder and try to be the teacher's pet."

Percy gave Cyrus a big grin. The boys took off like young colts as each went toward his home.

One bright Saturday not long after this encounter Cyrus rode over on Peacock to see Percy and to play.

All the boys at the Field School this spring had spent a lot of time playing marbles. They were not allowed to play near the schoolhouse, because the teacher would not believe that they were not playing for "keeps."

That did not bother the boys too much. They had a place set up a few rods down the road from the schoolhouse. It was in the section of the woods where they were sure the teacher would not see them.

Cyrus had a good collection of marbles. His Uncle William had just given him some that he had had when he was a boy. The agates were his special prize. They were so clear you could almost see through them.

The boys had marked a big circle on the ground. Then, when they were ready to play,

they put clay marbles they called *commys* into the big ring.

Cyrus spread out his bag of marbles. He could not decide which of the three agates he would use today for the shooter.

At last he picked out a cream-colored agate. Taking the marble between his thumb and forefinger, he shot at the other marbles. The agate struck the *commys* with such force that two of the clay marbles rolled outside the ring.

"Gee," Percy said, "that agate really can shoot the *commys*."

"It's a good one, all right," Cyrus said.

When it was Percy's turn, he didn't shoot at all well.

"Let me borrow that cream-colored agate," Percy said hopefully.

So Cyrus gave him his agate.

It was a good thing the boys were not playing for keeps, for Cyrus was doing unusually well.

"I'd sure like to have a smooth agate like the one you are using," Percy said, rolling Cyrus's agate in his hand. Then he got down on the ground and shot at the *commys*. He hit two of them. The clay marbles rolled outside the ring.

"I might be a champion if I had a smooth round marble like yours," Percy hinted.

"It's mine," Cyrus said. "It came from Germany. At least Uncle William, who gave it to me, said it did."

"Maybe you would trade it," Percy suggested.

"Well, maybe," Cyrus said slowly. "What do you have to trade?"

"A hunting knife that has a real sharp blade," Percy said. "Do you want to see it?"

"Well, I guess so." Cyrus was not too anxious to trade his prized agate.

Percy ran into the house and came back with the knife. He pulled it out of the sheath.

It was a good knife, and Cyrus was impressed.

Percy handed it to Cyrus so that he could look at it more carefully. He turned it over and over, and then ran his finger along the blade.

"Does this knife belong to you?" Cyrus asked.

"My grandfather gave it to me, but I don't like to hunt. I want to be the champion marble player in the Valley of Virginia. I want your agate."

Cyrus still had not decided whether he really wanted to trade his cream-colored agate, but he liked the knife very much. He thought for a long time. At last he said, "It's a deal. You can have my agate, and I'll take the knife."

"All I've needed was an agate shooter," Percy said, delighted with the trade. "Now I know I can be a champion."

"I still have two slick agates left," Cyrus said.

"And you have a special knife, too," Percy added quickly.

When he rode home on Peacock later that afternoon, Cyrus stopped by the kiln where his father was working. The sheath with the knife was attached to Cyrus's belt.

"Where did you get that knife?" his father asked harshly.

"From Percy Hader," Cyrus said.

Cyrus took the knife out of the sheath so that his father could look at it more closely.

His father turned it over several times.

"What did you do to get that knife?" Mr. McCormick asked, his voice severe.

"I traded it," Cyrus answered truthfully.

"What did you have of such great value that you could trade it to get this valuable knife?" his father asked.

"A marble, a beautiful cream agate," Cyrus replied.

"You mean one of the agates your Uncle William gave you a long time ago?" Mr. McCormick questioned indignantly.

Cyrus nodded.

Mr. McCormick shook his head. "Cyrus, I am disappointed in you," he said. "The agate was a gift from your uncle. You have no right to give it to someone else."

"I traded it for something I wanted," Cyrus answered.

"You do not sell a gift," his father insisted. "The knife is worth more than the agate. So it was not a fair trade."

"Percy suggested that we trade. He wanted

59

my cream-colored agate. He thinks this shooter will make him a champion marble player," Cyrus explained carefully.

"Trading can be one-sided, Son." Mr. McCormick said. "That's the reason we use money. Each coin is worth a certain amount, so when one buys an article, he knows exactly what it's worth. That is fair, value for value. But in a trade, one person is generally the loser."

Cyrus listened patiently to his father. He had to admit that his father was right.

Mr. McCormick continued, "The Dutch in New York traded a few bright-colored beads and some money for the whole island of Manhattan. Even though the Indians were pleased with the sparkling beads, the exchange still was not an even one. You know also that I do not approve of boys trading."

Cyrus hung his head. "But I like the knife," he said. His voice was low.

60

"You should," his father snapped. "You got the better trade." Mr. McCormick paused. "Son, there is only one thing you can do. You must go back right now, return the knife, and get your agate back from Percy."

That was final, Cyrus knew.

"Don't you do any more trading or swapping!" His father shook his finger at him.

Reluctantly Cyrus mounted Peacock. The knife in the sheath seemed heavy on his belt. He surely hated to give up that knife. He had to admit, though, that the knife was worth more than the cream agate.

As Peacock galloped along, Cyrus tried to think of a plan that would be satisfactory to Percy and himself. He hated to give up the knife.

Maybe there was a way——

"Percy," he called when he arrived at the Hader place. He jumped off Peacock.

Percy came running out of the house. "I surely

61

like my agate," the boy said. "I can hardly wait to win some games with it."

"I like the knife," Cyrus said, taking it out of the sheath. "But Papa does not approve of trades. He made me bring your knife back to you. Papa says I cannot make trades."

"I'm satisfied," Percy insisted. "This is the best agate in the whole country."

"I can't go against Papa," Cyrus tried to explain. "We'll have to forget that we ever traded. The knife belongs to you and the agate belongs to me." Cyrus spoke fast. "You keep the agate for awhile. Papa won't object to that, I know. When you get to be champion, then maybe you can buy some agates that are much better than this one."

"I don't quite understand," Percy said. "But if I can keep the agate for a while, that suits me fine." He scratched his head. "But what about the knife?" he asked.

"When I want to use it, I'll borrow it from you," Cyrus replied.

"All right," Percy nodded. "That's a promise."

"That's a promise," Cyrus said.

He mounted Peacock and rode toward Walnut Grove Plantation. "Maybe someday I can have Grandfather's knife," he thought.

Yankee Peddler

CYRUS SHINNIED up the largest tree along the driveway that led to the McCormick plantation. Sitting on one of the strong limbs, he held tight to the branches above him. It was a good feeling to be completely hidden by the heavy leaves.

"No one can see me," he said aloud. "This is my secret hiding place." He giggled happily.

Cyrus had only been there a few minutes when he heard a peculiar noise. It wasn't like any of the sounds around the farm. It sounded more like pots and pans hitting against wood.

Suddenly he smiled. "I should have known as soon as I heard that banging," he said to the walnut tree. "Of course! It's the Yankee peddler! It's Peddler Tom!"

He jumped down and ran toward the house as fast as his legs would carry him.

"The peddler is here," he called out excitedly. "Peddler Tom has come!"

The echo sounded down the long hall.

"Where?" his mother asked, as she hurried out of the kitchen.

"Down the road," Cyrus shouted.

Mrs. McCormick walked to the front of the house, followed by Susan and Robert.

Most of the members of the family were waiting impatiently in the driveway when the peddler pulled on the horse's reins.

"Whoa, there," Peddler Tom said.

The pots and pans stopped banging. Tom jumped out of the gaily decorated cart.

"Good day," said Tom in a high voice.

Cyrus saw that Tom's clothes were as shabby

and as soiled as they were on his visit last year. But the boy was fascinated by the long white beard that moved up and down when the peddler talked.

"I have many fine wares for the lady of the house," Tom said graciously, bowing low to Mrs. McCormick.

Cyrus's mother smiled. "I need some pins and needles," she said.

Cyrus knew that everyone in the family looked forward to the peddler's visit as much as he did. He walked around the wagon. There were dozens of shiny copper pots and pans hanging on hooks and nails.

"These copper pans will last a lifetime," Cyrus heard Tom tell his mother. The peddler reached for two of the shiniest pans. "You won't find better pans for your money than these," he said proudly. "They are the best bargain you will find in the whole country."

Cyrus smiled. He was sure the peddler was exaggerating, but he was a pleasant, jolly man.

"I think I'll take both of them," Mrs. McCormick suddenly announced. "That large one and the small one. We need more pans for cooking."

"Fine," the peddler said, smiling broadly. Cyrus could see that he was minus a number of teeth.

"I'll put the pans on the grass," Tom said, looking around. "You have a pretty place here. Your lawn is like velvet."

Mrs. McCormick smiled. Cyrus knew how proud his mother was of the well-cared-for lawn and the bright-colored flowers.

"Peacocks!" Tom exclaimed, as one of the beautiful birds strutted toward them. "They are the most handsome birds in the world, always so proud and dignified."

"I like my peacocks," Mrs. McCormick told him modestly.

Cyrus smiled again. He knew now that his mother would buy many more articles from Tom than she really needed. This peddler certainly knew how to flatter his customers.

Today the peacocks seemed much more curious about this stranger than they usually were about visitors to Walnut Grove Plantation. They walked slowly toward the cart and strutted more proudly with every mincing step.

Cyrus had to admit that they were not only handsome but graceful. The crested male had a magnificent green and gold train decorated with blue-green spots like eyes.

Cyrus never tired of watching them. His mother had once told Cyrus that there were many peacocks in India, but as far as he knew, these were the only peacocks in the Valley of Virginia.

Susan was looking at a tray filled with jewelry. She was fascinated.

"Mother, please come here. This necklace sparkles like diamonds!" she said.

Mrs. McCormick glanced at the many bright and sparkling pins and necklaces in the velvet-lined tray. "They are nice," she said.

"May I have one?" Susan teased.

"We'll see," her mother answered.

Susan and her mother stood for a long time admiring the sparkling jewelry. When Mr. Mc-Cormick walked over to them, Susan looked up. "Papa, I would be the happiest girl in the world if I could have one of these necklaces."

"I've picked out a pretty handkerchief for you," Mr. McCormick said. "If it is all right with your mother, you may also have the necklace if it does not cost too much."

"Thank you, Papa," Susan said happily. "I want to show this necklace to Eunice and Hannah." She turned around and ran quickly into the house.

Cyrus knew that after the servants had admired it, she would disappear into the big bedroom that had a full-length mirror.

"Susan will stand in front of the mirror for the next half hour," Cyrus said. "Girls are funny." He shook his head. "Only a girl could get excited about something fancy like a sparkling necklace."

"Susan is interested in the things that make her pretty," Cyrus's mother answered sympathetically, "and you are interested in the tools in the shop."

"And Papa's reaper," Cyrus added.

"I know you are." Mrs. McCormick sighed, but Cyrus caught a look of hope in his mother's eyes.

Mrs. McCormick looked at other articles the peddler had. She picked up several spools of silk and cotton thread, some yards of gray cotton, a few pieces of lace. She also picked up several small packages of needles and pins, as well as a few boxes of spices.

She turned to Tom. "There are a number of articles I would like to purchase if you will give me a fair price."

Cyrus was not too curious about the cost of the things his mother wanted, so he walked over to the other side of the wagon. He found several articles that interested him.

"Papa," Cyrus asked, "may I buy that lead pencil and some sheets of paper?"

"If that is what you want, Son." Mr. McCormick nodded.

"I need them," Cyrus said. "I want to sketch an idea or two."

Mr. McCormick took a leather pouch from the side pocket of his trousers. After he had paid the peddler, he said, "I guess that's all this time. We'll see you on your next trip."

"Yes, sir." Tom put the money in his dirty

leather bag. He started to gather up his wares and to put them in place in the cart. "I'll see you next year," he said.

Mr. McCormick walked toward the blacksmith shop.

"Where are you going?" Cyrus asked the peddler.

"Somewhere beyond the Valley of Virginia," Tom answered, as he got into the cart and picked up the reins.

"I've never been over the ridge," Cyrus said.

"There are green valleys, and then farther west there are even more wide-open spaces. Prairies, they call that land that stretches for miles and miles," Tom told Cyrus.

"Are there many people living on the prairies?" Cyrus asked.

"More people are moving farther west all the time," Tom answered. "Land is mighty cheap, so they can raise more crops."

"Then those farmers need Papa's reaper," Cyrus said.

"What's a reaper?" the peddler asked.

"It's a big machine that cuts grain faster than a man can cut with his sickle," the boy said.

"Farmers would welcome a machine that would make harvesting easier," Tom said. "They all complain about the hard work, especially when the grain is ready to be harvested."

"Then maybe you could sell the reaper," Cyrus said hopefully.

"Well, maybe." The peddler scratched his head. "If it's a big machine, I wouldn't be able to put it in this wagon. But tell me more about your papa's reaper."

Suddenly Cyrus was tongue-tied. The reaper was very real to him, but he suddenly remembered that it had failed in the last field test. Maybe the reaper never would cut grain.

"Will you show me the machine?" Tom asked.

74

Cyrus shook his head. "It doesn't work right," he answered.

"Oh." Tom shrugged his shoulders. He didn't seem as interested in the reaper as he had been a few minutes earlier.

Cyrus wished now he had not said anything about the reaper that stood covered with dust in the blacksmith shop. If his father knew he had mentioned it to the peddler, he probably would not like it. Mr. McCormick might even punish him. The boy bit his tongue.

Tom suddenly changed the subject. "You say, Son, that you have never been beyond this valley?"

"That's right, sir," Cyrus answered.

"You seem like a bright lad," Tom said, studying Cyrus. "How about coming along with me?" he suggested. "I get mighty lonely in the evenings, especially now that my dog Chief is too old to make this journey." He paused. "I could come back this way in about a week. Then we would have plenty of time for you to tell me about this new machine." Tom pulled on his long beard.

"I'd have to get permission from my parents," Cyrus said.

"Of course, of course," Tom agreed.

Cyrus wanted to say, "Yes," at once. Then he would get to see country over the ridge that he had never seen. Maybe he could see for himself what the land looked like that people called the "Prairie." Here was his chance.

But there were many duties on the farm these days. There was a chance, too, that his father might work once again on the machine. Maybe Cyrus could help him. That reaper meant everything to Cyrus.

"Thank you, sir," Cyrus said. "I can't go with you this time. Maybe next year, if you offer me the chance."

76

"All right, Son," Tom said, "but I would like to have you with me right now."

"My father needs me," Cyrus said, truthfully.

"I'll see you on my next trip," Tom said as he jerked on the reins. "Giddap, there, Old Girlie," he called to his horse.

Cyrus dug his feet into the cool green grass and watched the cart until it disappeared from sight. He still could hear the faint sound of the pans banging on the side of the wagon.

"Someday our reaper will cut the grain on the prairies far beyond the ridge," Cyrus said to the big walnut trees. "And there will be many peddlers selling the reaper."

He hurried toward the blacksmith shop.

Brother Trouble

CYRUS HAD decided quite some time ago that younger brothers were a nuisance. His sister Susan did not bother him. She liked her dolls and played house under the trees by herself, but Robert wanted to do the same things Cyrus did.

Jo had often said, "Cyrus, you are too impatient with Robert."

Cyrus hunched his shoulders. He did not like to have Jo criticize him. "Younger brothers are a nuisance," Cyrus insisted.

"Robert is only two years younger than you are," Jo tried to explain. "He wants to do the same things you do because you are his big

78

brother. He is proud of you. He wants to be like you in every way."

Cyrus had not been aware of this. "I still don't like it," he said. "Robert asks too many questions. He makes me tired. Anyway I don't want a twin, and I don't want him to mimic me!"

One day Cyrus decided to go fishing. He and Jo raced each other to the barn to get the fishhooks and line. They had been there only a few minutes when they heard footsteps. Cyrus turned around. There stood his younger brother, smiling expectantly.

"What are you doing?" Robert asked.

"Getting some fishhooks," Cyrus mumbled. He was tempted to fib, but it was too obvious what he and Jo were doing.

"I want to go fishing, too," Robert said.

Cyrus's first thought was to tell his brother that he could not go with them. But that was being selfish. After all, he didn't own the stream. If he said, "No," Robert would probably run back to the house to tell their mother. Then she might decide that the boys could not go fishing this afternoon. That would be disappointing.

"Well, all right," Cyrus said, but he was disgusted. "You'll have to find your own fishing rod when we get to the woods. We'll be looking for green branches to make ours. We're going to have to make some new ones."

"That suits me," Robert agreed. "I'll need hooks and a line."

"I'll carry the hooks so they won't jab us as we walk through the underbrush," Jo said.

"Do you have to think of that?" Cyrus asked. At this point he was annoyed with Jo as well as his brother.

"I can't let you get hurt if there is any way to prevent it," Jo said calmly. "That's what your father and mother have told me many times."

"I can take care of myself," Cyrus said.

"I know you can," Jo nodded.

In a few minutes they started for the woods.

Jo and Cyrus climbed up one of the trees to pick out some limbs that would serve as fishing rods. They found two good branches, but could not find a third one.

"We're wasting a lot of time," Cyrus said. He was impatient. He looked up at the dark sky. "It's going to rain, and we don't even have our rods ready."

"I don't like to fish in the rain," Robert complained.

"It doesn't make any difference to the fish," Cyrus said. "They are always wet in the water."

Jo laughed. He thought Cyrus's answer to his brother was really funny.

"But I don't like to get wet," Robert said seriously.

"Didn't you say you wanted to go fishing?" Cyrus asked.

"Ye-es." Robert sounded doubtful.

"Well, we're going to fish in the rain," Cyrus informed him. "You can go home if you want to."

Jo spoke up. "You know your mother does not like you to wear wet clothes. Let's go fishing another day."

"If we hadn't had to look for a pole for Robert,"

Cyrus said resentfully, "probably by now we would have caught at least two fish."

"Another day we might even have better luck," Jo said cheerfully.

Cyrus started to jump down from the tall tree. As he did so, he twisted his ankle as he fell on the ground. "Ouch!" he cried.

Jo, who had climbed down ahead of Cyrus, rushed with Robert over to the injured boy.

"I hope you didn't break any bones," Jo said. He was worried.

Cyrus felt his ankle and foot. "No," he said, "nothing seems to be broken, thank goodness, but I don't think I can walk very well."

Jo and Robert helped Cyrus as he tried to walk.

"My ankle won't do what I want it to do," Cyrus said.

"We'll make a chair and carry you home," Robert offered.

"Guess you'll have to," Cyrus said. This time he spoke kindly to his younger brother.

"I'm glad Robert came with us," Jo said as the two boys crossed their arms and Cyrus put his arms around their sturdy shoulders.

It was a long slow walk from the woods back to the house.

"Sometimes younger brothers can be helpful," Cyrus said.

He wished now he had never complained about Robert.

Cyrus and His Grandfather

GRANDFATHER McCORMICK and Cyrus were good friends. They often took long walks through the woods where the young boy learned much about the birds and the trees.

One day when they were in the deep forest, a bluebird flew out of the walnut tree just as Cyrus and his grandfather came by.

"That bluebird has a nest in that tree," Grandfather McCormick said, "but don't look for it."

"I want to see how many eggs there are in that nest," Cyrus said. He headed for the large tree.

"Cyrus," his grandfather called, his voice stern. "Let the birds alone."

"Why?" Cyrus asked, turning around.

"Birds don't like people to find their nests with their eggs or baby birds. You remember this tree, and in a few weeks we'll come back. We'll watch the mother bird teach her babies to fly then."

"All right," Cyrus said, but he still wanted to look for the nest.

Cyrus studied the tree more carefully. He spoke thoughtfully. "Grandpa, I won't forget this tree. The bluebird has built her nest in the black walnut where I carved my initial when I was five years old."

"Let's see," Grandfather McCormick said as he walked over to look for Cyrus's initial.

"You did a fine job of carving," his grandfather said, patting the boy on his shoulders.

"Jo helped me," Cyrus hastened to explain. "The wood was hard, and I got tired after I had made the C."

86

"Jo helps you in many ways," his grandfather smiled fondly at Cyrus.

"Yes." Cyrus nodded. "He warned me, too, about being careful with the knife. It was sharp, and he didn't want it to slip."

"I'm glad to hear that," Grandfather McCormick said. "A farm boy has to learn when he is

87

young to be careful of sharp blades. But he needs to know at an early age how to use a knife."

"You and Papa agree on that," Cyrus said.

"You must consider this your special tree," Grandfather McCormick said.

"I do." Cyrus nodded.

"And the bluebird picked this tree from all the other trees in the woods to build her nest." He paused. "That's a good sign."

"How?" Cyrus asked, puzzled.

Grandfather McCormick took off his old hat and rubbed his head. "There's an old tale from Europe about the bluebird," he said. "People believe that it brings happiness and luck. These bluebirds chose your tree, so if you do not harm them, you'll probably have good luck all through your life."

"I hope so," Cyrus said looking up at the tree. It surely had grown a lot in four years.

"But that doesn't mean you'll have success

without working for it," his grandfather added quickly.

"I like to work," Cyrus said.

"Yes, I believe you do." His grandfather nodded. "Hard work never hurt anyone." He glanced at the sky that had already turned dark gray. "Guess we better start back before the sky opens up and pours water on us. Anyway we've had a pleasant time in the woods today."

"Yes," Cyrus agreed smilingly.

They hurried as fast as they could through the woods, but it began raining sharply.

"It's surely raining cats and dogs," Grandfather McCormick said.

"Let's stop under this big old tree, Grandpa," Cyrus suggested as he tried to squeeze the rain from his wet hair.

They leaned against the tree and watched the rain coming down in torrents.

Suddenly Cyrus looked at his grandfather.

"What does it mean when you say it's raining cats and dogs?" he asked.

His grandfather chuckled. "That is sort of an odd expression, isn't it?" He paused. "That also comes from the old country." He laughed to himself. "Well, in the cities like London and Dublin where there is so much dirt in the gutters, the heavy rains would sweep the garbage out of the streets and gutters, including all the dead cats and dogs."

"Oh," Cyrus said. "Those places must smell."

"They do," Grandfather McCormick agreed.

When the rain finally stopped, the boy and his grandfather walked through the puddles of water to the house.

Cyrus's mother opened the door. "I'm glad you're finally back here," she said. "You are both wet to the skin. Both of you get dry clothes on, and by that time supper will be ready."

"Yes, Mama," Cyrus said. "But Grandpa and

I had a wonderful time in the woods until it started to rain."

"And then it rained cats and dogs," Grandfather McCormick said, winking at the boy.

"That cloudburst had the biggest cats and dogs I ever hope to see," Cyrus answered as he hurried to change into dry clothes.

The Chest with Two Keys

It RAINED that night and the following day. The house was dark and damp. Cyrus was restless. He was tired of hearing the constant pounding of the rain as it splashed on the roof.

He had wanted to be with his father at the shop, but his mother had said he would be in the way.

Cyrus was disappointed and unhappy. He did not want to play with Susan and Robert because they were as restless as he was.

Even though there were acres of land around the log house, the McCormick home was much too small for the growing family.

Cyrus did not have a room of his own, and he could never be sure that the things he prized would be safe under his bed. His brothers and sisters were always curious about his treasures.

This Saturday morning he decided he would draw a picture of the Baltimore oriole's nest he had found on the ground a few days ago. He had put the bird's nest in the big box under his bed where he kept special articles. He had some old coins his Uncle William had given him, some odd-shaped stones he had found by the river, and his marbles.

When he looked in the box this morning, he could not find the oriole's nest. He rechecked the other things, and they seemed to be there.

He ran to his mother. "Where's my bird's nest?" he demanded.

"Your bird's nest?" she asked. "What do you mean?"

"I found an oriole's nest on the ground in the

woods," Cyrus said, speaking rapidly. "I put it in the wooden box under my bed, along with my other treasures, but it isn't there now."

"Maybe Jo knows where it is," Mrs. McCormick said calmly.

But Jo did not know.

Cyrus didn't think he would. Cyrus had not told Jo about his secret hiding place under the bed. He didn't think it was necessary for Jo to know. For that matter he didn't think anyone knew about that place.

Cyrus walked slowly into the kitchen. His baby brother was sitting near the fireplace playing with something that looked like straw.

"That's mine, give it to me," Cyrus said, attempting to take it from the little boy.

The youngster started to cry. "Mine, mine," he said, holding tight to the nest.

Hearing the younger children cry made Cyrus nervous. It was no use trying to take the bird's nest from his baby brother. The best way to get the nest would be to give him something else to interest him.

Cyrus reached in his pocket for a ball of string. "Here is something that you will have fun rolling on the floor," he said.

Cyrus got down on the floor and rolled the ball toward his little brother. "See the big ball," he said, "it will roll all over the kitchen."

His brother was interested in the new toy. He forgot about the nest and crawled over to pick up the ball of string.

"Ball," he said, dropping the oriole's nest.

Cyrus picked it up and went over to the table to draw a sketch of the nest.

Later that morning, Grandfather McCormick came over to the table where Cyrus was working. "I have something to show you," he said.

Cyrus followed his grandfather into his room and over to a large oak chest.

"Your mother has just told me that the other children know where you keep your treasures," Grandfather McCormick said.

"That's right, Grandpa," Cyrus answered. "Now I don't have a safe place in this house to keep my things."

"I've been thinking, Cyrus," Grandfather Mc-Cormick said, "that maybe you would like to keep your things in this old chest of mine."

Cyrus's eyes almost popped.

"I have an extra key I can give you," Grandfather McCormick explained. "You can put this key on a nail in the barn, way up high, so that your brothers and sisters cannot reach it. Then no one but you and me can get in the chest. How would you like that?" he asked.

"Then my things will really be safe," Cyrus said delighted. "Thank you, Grandfather."

"I'll unlock the chest right now," Grandfather McCormick said.

When his grandfather lifted the heavy top, Cyrus caught a whiff of camphor.

"That keeps the moths out," his grandfather explained. "I keep some of my clothes in here. Then I have some old books and some other things. You may put your things here."

What interested Cyrus especially was a white wig that his grandfather had once worn on some important occasion. There was also a gold ring that had a family crest.

"Grandfather," Cyrus said. He was thinking. He did not want to hurt his grandfather's feelings, but he felt having a key to the oak chest was too much of a responsibility. "I want you to keep the key," Cyrus said. "I might lose it. When I want to get something from the big chest, I'll ask you for the key."

"I wouldn't want you to lose the key," his grandfather agreed. "Maybe for the time being I'll just keep it, but remember that I am letting you have a section in this chest for your very own. Your treasures will be safe now."

"Thank you," Cyrus said happily.

"I know how a boy feels," Grandfather McCormick said kindly. "Everyone needs a special place to keep his treasures. Since you are my oldest grandchild, I can do this and feel that I'm not being partial to you."

He gave Cyrus a big wink.

Cyrus smiled. He knew that his grandfather liked him very much. Cyrus hurried to get his treasures from the big box under his bed.

Through the weeks Grandfather McCormick and Cyrus shared many happy hours as well as sharing the big oak chest.

Cyrus especially enjoyed standing by the big loom and watching his grandfather weave. He was weaving wool thread into cloth for the McCormick household.

"That is a wonderful idea," Cyrus said.

"What's a wonderful idea?" His grandfather looked up from his weaving.

"The loom you are using," Cyrus answered.

"It's slow work, just like it is slow using the sickles to harvest the grain," Grandfather McCormick said.

"There's a man by the name of Samuel Slater," he went on, "who worked in the textile mills in England, but he wanted to come to this country. He left England in disguise, since textile workers were not permitted to leave the country."

"Mr. Slater memorized all the parts of the machinery that wove cotton cloth. When he arrived in America, he made the necessary parts and assembled them into a machine. Now he has a big cotton mill, maybe two of them, up in Rhode Island."

Grandfather McCormick paused, and looked at Cyrus. "I say that in this big country where there is so much land, the farmers need a reaper

100

to help them harvest their grain, just as Slater's machine has helped the people working with cotton. That's why I wish your father would work more on that idea he has."

"He has so many other things to do," Cyrus said, seriously.

"Yes, I know," Grandfather McCormick agreed. "But when a man gets an idea like your papa's, it's almost an obligation for him to keep at it until it works."

Cyrus's grandfather went back to his weaving and the young boy watched him, fascinated with the expert way he worked.

"I know you are mighty interested in this reaper," Grandfather McCormick said. Then he stopped weaving and turned around to look at his grandson.

"Cyrus, if your father can't figure out a way to make his reaper work, then maybe you can when you are a little bit older."

"I think Papa will figure out a way," Cyrus said hopefully.

"But if he doesn't, then maybe you can," his grandfather insisted. "You seem to have inherited some of your father's ability and interest to experiment. That's good. Someone in the McCormick family has to make the reaper work." He nodded. "I think it will be you who will invent the McCormick reaper, the farmer's friend!"

"Farmer's friend," Cyrus whispered. "That reaper would be the best friend a farmer could have."

"Mind you, don't forget what I've said to you today." Grandfather McCormick touched the boy's broad shoulder.

The Globe

CYRUS WAS delighted when his mother asked him to ride over the the minister's home on an errand. He might even get a chance to see the globe his father had told him about seeing there.

"Peacock and I will get the book," Cyrus said. He hurried out of the house and over to the barn to saddle his horse.

The boy raced Peacock over the rolling countryside. When they reached the Morrison place, Cyrus jumped down and tied Peacock to the hitching post. Then he walked up the path to the porch that almost circled the house. He knocked on the front door.

"Good afternoon, Mrs. Morrison," Cyrus said politely, when the minister's wife came to the door. He had taken off his wide black hat and was now holding it in his hand.

"Won't you come in, Cyrus?" Mrs. Morrison asked. She smiled as she opened the door wide.

"I'm here on an errand," Cyrus explained. "Reverend Morrison has offered to lend a book to my father. He mentioned it at church Sunday and said it would be ready any time."

"Then we'll go right to his study where my husband is working," Mrs. Morrison said.

Cyrus followed her through several large rooms to where the minister sat at his desk, writing. Cyrus guessed he was working on the sermon he would hear next Sunday morning. The McCormicks were religious and were loyal supporters of the church.

"Cyrus, you are getting to be a tall young man," the minister said after he had greeted the thirteen-year-old boy, and Cyrus had explained his errand.

"I'm growing almost too fast," the boy said, "I feel like I'm all arms and legs."

The minister laughed. "All of us have to go through that stage. It's part of growing up."

Cyrus had always liked the Reverend Morrison, and now he liked him better than ever. He seemed to understand that awkward age that Cyrus was now experiencing.

A few minutes later the minister walked over to one of the mahogany bookcases with glass doors. "Maybe you would like to look at some of my books," the minister said.

Cyrus's eyes sparkled. "Thank you, sir, but if you don't mind, I would like to study the globe Papa has told me you have."

"Of course," the Reverend Morrison said.

Cyrus had never seen a globe before. He turned it around slowly, looking for the United

States. Virginia was marked. Cyrus was proud of the fact that his state was one of the thirteen original colonies. He noticed that beyond the Mississippi River there were few marks, only a few rivers were identified.

The teacher at school had talked about the Louisiana Purchase, but it was not indicated on the globe. The countries in Europe were all there, printed in black letters.

The Reverend Morrison, who had been searching in one of his bookcases, now came over to Cyrus. He did not disturb Cyrus's studying.

Cyrus turned toward the gray-haired man. "Sir, a globe gives a much better picture of the world than a map does," he said. "It's so round. You really know how the world looks."

"A globe is more accurate than a map," the minister agreed, smiling. "Every school should have one, but the price is dear. A friend of mine sent this one to me from England."

"I wish we had a globe at the Field School," Cyrus said. "Then I know I would be much more interested in geography."

"You probably would be," the minister agreed. "Here's the book for your father."

"Thank you, Reverend Morrison," Cyrus said taking the book. The minister walked with the boy to the door.

On the way home, Cyrus kept thinking about the globe. This was one time when he did not want Peacock to race. His mind was busy.

How could he get a globe for his school? Right now he didn't know, but he was going to try to figure out a way.

There wasn't very much equipment in the classroom, just an oak desk for the teacher, some rough benches for the pupils to sit on, a half dozen slates, a few books, and a large flat map. Maybe he could make a globe. He thought about how he could do it all the way home.

Jo was waiting at the barn for Cyrus when he came back from the Morrison place.

"I have a wonderful idea," Cyrus said, as he pulled on the reins for Peacock to stop. "Jo, if you'll unsaddle Peacock and water him, then I can start working on my plan right now."

"What do you have up your sleeve this time?" Jo asked as he took hold of the reins.

Cyrus smiled. "I'll tell you later. I'll be working under the walnut tree."

"You look so wise," Jo said and smiled.

Cyrus raced to the house for paper and the quill pen and ink. He sat down in a cool shady spot under the big old tree with his legs crossed. He immediately started to make a rough sketch of the globe.

He was excited. Now he might be able to understand more about the shape of the earth. The schoolmaster had explained many times that the earth was not flat but round. Then the teacher would point to the map, and the countries and oceans looked flat to Cyrus.

He had learned in his history that people were sure if Columbus sailed too far, he would come to the edge of the world and fall off. Not until he had seen the globe at the minister's house had Cyrus realized that the earth was really round.

"What's your new idea?" Jo asked as he sat down beside his friend.

"A globe."

"What's a globe?" Jo asked. He did not go to school, but worked all day on the plantation.

"A round model of the earth," Cyrus explained patiently. "It's really like a map that shows the continents, the countries, and the waters of the world. But a globe is round like a ball instead of being flat like maps."

"What will you use the globe for?" Jo asked, peering down at Cyrus's rough sketch.

"To learn where the countries of the world are located."

"Oh," Jo said.

"The globe will have to have a good strong base to support it," Cyrus said, studying the drawing carefully.

"I'll want to see this globe when it is finished," Jo said eagerly.

110

"That will be a long time." Cyrus shook his head. "I guess wood will be heavy enough for a base to hold the globe."

Cyrus drew a square at the base of the globe he had sketched. "I want to be able to turn it," he said, "but I don't exactly know how to work that out."

"If you have a steel rod that goes through the globe," Jo suggested, "and it is attached to the base, then the globe will turn."

"I guess it will," Cyrus said slowly. He was thinking hard. Then he looked up and smiled. "Jo, you have some right good ideas."

"Supper!" Jo's mother called from the doorway of the log house.

"Guess we have to eat." Cyrus sighed, as he folded the paper and put it in his hip pocket. "I would much rather work on the globe."

The boys hurried in to eat, but Cyrus kept planning how he could make a globe.

The following Monday, Cyrus talked to one of the boys at school about the globe. His friend studied the drawing for a long time. Then he scratched his head. "What material are you going to use?" he asked.

"Cloth, maybe," Cyrus answered. "I might even tear up pieces of paper and mix it with flour paste. I think it's called papier-mâché."

"Sounds like a mighty big job," the boy said. "Don't count on me to help you."

"I guess it is a big job," Cyrus admitted. "I hope the globe will work."

"Why don't you ask the schoolmaster?" the boy asked.

Cyrus shook his head. "I want to work this problem out by myself," he said. "If the globe comes out the way I hope, then I will show it to him. I want us to use it at school."

But Cyrus was worried. Maybe the globe was too big a job, but he was not giving up.

112

"I'm going to think about this globe some more," Cyrus said to the trees that afternoon as he walked along the road from the Field School to his home.

After supper, when he was in the living room, Cyrus happened to notice the round feet on the side table.

"That's what I'll do," he announced to Jo, later. "I'll make the globe of wood. I'll use the trunk of the rotted oak tree that the wind blew down last winter. I'll make the wood round like a big ball." Cyrus smiled. "You know, Jo, I really think I'm on the right track this time."

"I hope you are," Jo answered.

Some days later the boys had one of the work horses on the plantation drag the big tree trunk from the woods to the shop.

"You're doing all right, old boy," Cyrus said to the horse, as he patted his long nose. "You have saved Jo and me a lot of hard work."

"We would have had a tough time carrying that old tree," Jo said as he walked along, following the horse.

As Cyrus patiently smoothed the wood with a plane, and then whittled it, he wondered whether it was worth all the time that he was having to put into it. If he didn't hurry, the school term would be over before the globe was finished.

He hoped it would work, but he still had not experimented with the steel rod that Jo had suggested. If the globe wouldn't turn easily, he would have to work out another idea.

At last the big round ball of hard wood was smooth and shiny. Cyrus could hardly wait to outline the continents in black ink and to print the names of the countries and oceans. With great care he sketched the continents on a large piece of paper so that he would not make many mistakes when he painted them on wood.

ew months when Cyrus dreaded
ol.

ike your tutor, Cyrus," his mother
d been studying the globe while
nick had been talking to Cyrus. "I
p your globe here at home, so all of
more about the world."

I'm pleased that you like the globe,"
smiling.

do, Son," she said. "I already have
cked out where we will put it. Come
she beckoned.

ollowed her into the big room in the
he house.

r best room?" Cyrus asked.

his mother nodded. "We will put it on
ogany pie table that belonged to your
other Hall."

s was delighted. Even though he had
planned to give the globe to the school,

One morning when Jo was helping, Cyrus
said, "Someday I'm going to see the world. I
want to see many of the places I'm putting on
the globe."

"How are you going to do it?" Jo asked. He
was practical from the top of his curly black
head to the tip of his toes.

There was a serious tone in his voice when
Cyrus answered, "I'll have a business that will
take me to many countries across the ocean."

"What business will that be?" Jo asked. He
was curious to hear Cyrus's answer.

"I hope it will be the reaper," Cyrus said, looking off into the distance. "Farmers in other parts
of the world need Papa's reaper as much as the
farmers do here in Virginia."

"It's too bad Mister Robert hasn't made it
work," Jo answered, shaking his head.

Cyrus nodded. He didn't tell Jo that he had
his own idea about a reaper that he hoped would

115

really work. Right now he must think and work on his new globe.

At last Cyrus finished making the globe. When Cyrus showed the finished globe to his parents, they were impressed with the fine work.

"Jo gave me some good ideas," Cyrus said, wanting his friend to be included in the praise he was receiving. "I know now where most of the countries of the world are. I hope the schoolmaster will like the globe."

"Of course he will," his father assured him. "Did you make it for the schoolmaster?"

"No," Cyrus said slowly. "Only I hope he will use it to make geography lessons more interesting for all the students. Now we can look for countries and oceans on the globe instead of on the old map."

"You take the globe to school with you tomorrow," Mr. McCormick said. "The students will like it." He looked at his wife. "Don't you

116

think this is the
he asked.

Mrs. McCorm

"For quite som
mother and I have
At last we have fou
young man. He wi
and mathematics."

"Then I won't be
any longer," Cyrus sai
seeing my friends."

"You will like Mr.
"He knows his subjects

"He won't be too strict

"Not if you will study a
father assured him.

Cyrus would welcome a
too strict and who did not
often. Maybe he wouldn't
much if he had a good tutor.

in the past f
going to scho
"You will
said. She h
Mr. McCorn
want to kee
us can learn
"Mother,
Cyrus said
"I surely
a place pi
with me,"
Cyrus
front of t
"In ou
"Yes,"
the mah
Grandm
Cyru
really

118

his mother's idea was much better. Now he could keep it.

When Cyrus showed the globe to the schoolmaster, he seemed to like it. But Cyrus was not too surprised with his comment.

"You should have been studying your lessons instead of wasting your time making this." The instructor's voice had a sharp note.

Cyrus wanted to tell him that he had not really taken time from his studying, but had given up other things that meant a great deal to him, like fishing and riding Peacock. He did not dare speak so boldly to the schoolmaster.

Now Cyrus was really glad that his parents had found a tutor for him. He was sure he would not miss this cross schoolmaster. Cyrus was glad that he had only a few more days in the Field School.

The following week Cyrus began his school work at home. Cyrus liked Mr. White, his new tutor, the very first time he came to the house to give him lessons in surveying and mathematics.

Mr. White respected Cyrus and encouraged him to be more resourceful in his creative work than he had been.

Cyrus especially liked surveying. Mr. White made him realize its value in a country like the United States of America. There was so much new land that had not yet been surveyed. He also told Cyrus about George Washington's experience as a surveyor when he was a young man. Cyrus dreamed of being a surveyor, too.

Cyrus showed Mr. White the new globe. Mr. White admired Cyrus's work.

The understanding tutor commented, "Cyrus, you have done an excellent job. You not only figured out a way to make a globe, but you also kept working at it until you had finished it. You have that 'something' which make people successful. You can do great deeds someday."

120

"Thank you, sir," Cyrus answered respectfully.

"I know you must have many more good ideas in that head of yours. It is up to you to experiment and invent and to follow through. America needs boys like you!" Mr. White suggested.

"I'd like to help Papa with his reaper to make the farmer's life easier," Cyrus said.

In Trouble
with Papa

IN THE LOG house that was much too small for the McCormick family, Cyrus could not find a room where his family could not hear him when he played his fiddle. His family never objected, but he was embarrassed to have an audience. Often he went out in the woods to practice on his fiddle.

He would not have been able to tell anyone exactly how he felt about his fiddle. But it was very special to him.

With the exception of Jo Anderson, Cyrus did not have any close friends. He considered his fiddle a very special friend.

One day in the early spring a grinder came to the plantation to sharpen the knives and scissors. As he made his grindstone whirl, he sang. One song that Cyrus liked was "Yankee Doodle."

Cyrus ran into the house to get his fiddle. "Will you please sing 'Yankee Doodle' again?" he asked. "I'll play the fiddle while you sing."

The grinder nodded and sang some other verses that Cyrus had never heard before. Cyrus enjoyed learning a new song. This one had plenty of rhythm. After the grinder had gone on his way, Cyrus sang the new song many times.

Then there was the song, "The Star-Spangled Banner," that his uncle had told him about. A young man by the name of Francis Scott Key had written the words when the bombs were bursting high in the air. Because his Uncle William had fought in the War of 1812, Cyrus liked this song especially well. His uncle would sing the words and Cyrus would play his fiddle.

But the most fun came when Jo and Cyrus were together. Jo had a good voice and knew many spirituals. He liked singing when Cyrus played the fiddle. Jo did not like to sing either, if he thought members of the family were listening. That was why the boys liked their "hideout" in the woods. It was a long ways from the house and barn.

One day when they were having a better time than usual, Cyrus suddenly had an idea about their music.

"Next week is Mother's birthday," he announced. "Let's surprise her."

"How can we surprise your mother?" Jo asked.

"I'm sure Mother has no idea how much fun we have with our music," Cyrus said. "We'll surprise her by singing some songs, and I'll play the fiddle. We'll sing 'Happy Birthday' to her."

"That's fine," Jo said, "but we should practice some more."

After they had sung "Happy Birthday" several times, Cyrus said, "That really isn't a very long song."

"No, it isn't," Jo agreed.

"We can make our program longer by starting with 'Happy Birthday,'" Cyrus said, "then singing 'The Star-Spangled Banner' and ending with 'Yankee Doodle.'"

"That sounds like a good idea," Jo said, "but we better practice just the way we plan to do it."

They weren't satisfied that day, but by the morning of Mrs. McCormick's birthday, the boys were ready.

That evening they sang the songs, with Cyrus playing on his fiddle.

Mrs. McCormick was surprised and pleased. "Please sing those songs again," she said.

As the wood crackled in the fireplace, the boys sang the songs again.

"We must have more evenings like this," Cyrus's mother said. "You boys practice on some other songs so that at the next cornhusking, you can play and sing." She paused and looked away. "When we have a larger house, we'll be able to invite more people to our home because we'll have more room. They will enjoy your music as much as I have. Thank you, boys," she said throwing them a kiss.

126

Cyrus was very happy to have pleased his mother. His parents were hard working people, and Cyrus wanted to help his mother and his father. He thought about the fun as he went about his work each day.

Cyrus was proud of his strong, healthy body. He could scarcely believe that he was growing up so fast. But his trousers were too short and his shoes were too tight for him.

"I need strong sons," Mr. McCormick said proudly one morning, as he tested the muscles in Cyrus's arms.

"There is more work to do all the time." He sighed. "If only there were machines to help, at least it would be easier on all of us." He looked directly at Cyrus. "Son," he said, "you surely do a good day's work in the fields. In fact, you get as much done as any grown man does."

Cyrus was glad that he could help his father, but he did not like the idea of all the hard work.

Everyone was up at sunrise, and they were all still working when the sun went down. Robert did his share these days, and the younger children also had chores to do.

Cyrus often got tired of working in the fields when it was hot. Today the sun burned his skin. Farming did not appeal to him the way tools did.

If only he could have one corner in the blacksmith shop that was his, he would be better satisfied. But the reaping machine took quite a bit of room.

Sometimes Cyrus was careless in putting the tools back in place. His father had warned him many times. Mr. McCormick had a place for every one of the tools he used, and he expected others who used his tools to be as careful as he was of them.

Late one afternoon when Cyrus was more uncomfortable than usual from the heat, he decided not to do any more work in the wheat field. He

128

glanced up and saw that Jo was busily raking at the far end. He would let Jo finish their work today in the field.

There was a job he wanted to do in the shop. Some bent nails should be straightened. His father had mentioned at breakfast that he would be at the kiln all day, so Cyrus thought this was a good time to straighten the nails. At least, he would not be in his father's way.

In the shop, Cyrus picked out a hammer and started to straighten out several nails. It was dark, so he decided to work outside in the shade of the old walnut tree. He used a flat stone to hammer on, and in no time at all he had straightened several dozen nails.

His mother came to the door of the log house. "Cyrus," she called, "I need you."

Cyrus left the hammer by the stone and ran toward the house to find out what his mother wanted. She sounded as if it were important.

"What is it, Mother?" he asked.

"The children don't seem to know what to do with themselves today. It is so hot, and I'm at my wit's end." She wiped her forehead with a handkerchief. "The baby is feverish, and I must take care of him. Will you play ball with the children but keep them in the shade?" she asked.

"Yes," Cyrus said. "I'll play ball with them."

When he was washing his face and hands that evening, getting ready for supper, his father came into the kitchen.

"Cyrus, where is the hammer with the hickory handle?" he asked.

"Don't you have several in the shop?" Mrs. McCormick asked.

"Yes, but I like this one the best," Mr. McCormick answered. "It is not in the niche where I always put it." His voice was sharp.

"I know where it is, Papa," Cyrus spoke up. "I'll get it for you."

His father followed him to the walnut tree in the yard.

"Cyrus, why didn't you put this hammer back where you found it?" Mr. McCormick asked, as his son handed it to him.

"I forgot," Cyrus admitted.

"That will never do," his father said. "If you cannot remember to put the tools back in their place, then you are not old enough to use them."

Cyrus had not seen his father so stern in a long time. He dreaded the punishment that he was sure he would get.

"The first rule of every good workman is to put his tools back where he found them," Mr. McCormick said. His voice was not quite so sharp now.

"Papa, I won't forget again," Cyrus said. He had learned his lesson, and he was quite sure he would remember about the tools from now on.

"I'm sorry, Son," his father said. "Perhaps the

only way you will learn is not to be permitted to use the tools for a week."

This was real punishment for Cyrus. For six days he couldn't go to the shop. In fact Mr. McCormick kept it locked and carried the key with him.

During that long period, Cyrus patiently marked off the hours until he would be permitted to work once again in the shop that meant everything to him.

Big New House

CYRUS'S MOTHER had talked about a larger house for quite some time. But Mr. McCormick did not feel that a new house was as important as his wife did. He was sentimental about the old log house which his father had built.

Cyrus was fond of it, too. This was the house where he was born. It held happy memories for him. He thought of how proud his Grandfather McCormick was of the old place. Grandfather McCormick had died four years ago in 1818, and Cyrus had been given the wonderful old chest. He kept the key in his hip pocket.

"Robert," Cyrus heard his mother say, "if we

don't build a larger house soon, the children will have to sleep outside on the ground. We just do not have enough rooms for our big family."

"We will build a house one of these days," Mr. McCormick promised.

"It isn't necessary to tear down the house we're living in," Mrs. McCormick said. "Why can't we build the new house next to this old one?"

"That's not a bad idea at all," Mr. McCormick said. "With the new house as well as this log one, we should have plenty of room."

"Yes, that would be fine," Mrs. McCormick said eagerly.

Actually the barn and the blacksmith shop were larger than the log house where the McCormick family lived. Cyrus was thirteen years old, and there were now six other children.

One evening when his father came into the kitchen for supper, Cyrus saw a twinkle in his eyes. He knew this meant something very good.

Cyrus could hardly wait, but he knew he would have to be patient. His father would not mention what was on his mind until after grace was said at the table and until the family almost finished the evening meal.

Suddenly his father said, "Mary Ann, how would you like a red brick house?" His eyes were even brighter than ever, Cyrus noticed.

"I would be pleased, Robert," she said happily, "to live in a big red brick house."

"I'm going to start this week or next," Mr. McCormick said. "In fact I've already done some sketches, but I know there are certain things you want."

"Right after supper I'll get my notes," Mrs. McCormick said eagerly. "Yes, I have many ideas for this new home where we will live the rest of our lives."

"A new house," Robert said, looking at his sister and brother, Susan and Cyrus.

135

"Maybe I'll have a room of my own," Susan hinted. She was tall for her nine years.

"Mary Caroline, we're going to have a red brick house," William said. He was seven and his sister was five years old.

"Red house," Leander and John, who were three and two years old, chimed in.

Cyrus was as excited as his brothers and sisters. When they all got up from the table, Cyrus hurried to the chest to get the paper and soft lead pencil he had bought from the peddler.

"The house will have a sixty-five-foot front, and it will be fifty feet deep," his father said as they sat around the big table in the kitchen.

It was going to be a lot of fun studying the sketches, and it would be wonderful to have a big red brick house. Cyrus was especially partial to red, because it was a bright, gay color.

Cyrus was even more excited when his father told him that he could make nails for the new

house. He had no idea how many that would be, but he knew one keg of nails weighed a hundred pounds.

Cyrus went with his father to the iron works to get the steel sheets. On the way over to the iron works, which was not too many miles from Walnut Grove Plantation, Mr. McCormick explained that steel nails would be used in the construction of the house, but that the wide floor boards would be nailed with wooden pegs.

Before Cyrus and Jo had pounded out more than two dozen nails, Robert was helping them, too. They needed him if they were to have enough kegs of nails ready for the workmen.

There was only one disturbing thought in Cyrus's mind about the new house. His father was so busy directing the men who were building the house and doing special jobs himself, that he did not have a free minute to think about the reaper now.

Many times Cyrus wanted to say something to his father, but he decided there was a time and place for everything. Right now was not the right time.

He wondered, though, when his father would experiment again with the "horse cradle," as the reaper was sometimes called. It collected more dust every day.

For a time everyone who worked on the plantation was busy bringing in stones from the fields. Cyrus, Jo, and Robert did their share of carrying rocks to the wagon.

As Mr. McCormick watched all the activity, he said, "This new house is a wonderful idea. We're getting two things done at the same time. We're clearing the fields of the rocks, and we're using them for the foundation."

The lime that was used to help keep the rocks in place came from the kiln at Walnut Grove.

After the foundation was laid, then the wooden frame went up. The wood had been cut from the McCormick woods.

Even though they were warned not to play about the wooden framework, Cyrus, Robert, and Jo wandered through it as often as they dared. They pretended to be living there.

Cyrus could very easily see how the house would look when it was completed, but Robert and Jo could not.

"I don't understand how you can tell what the house will look like when it is finished," Robert said, puzzled.

"Neither can I," Jo said.

"All I can see are the new boards and lots of air between them," Robert went on.

Cyrus laughed. "This will be the front door. There isn't a door here right now, but there will be. It will open onto a broad hallway." He pointed to some boards. "That's where the porch will be. The house will have eight big rooms, and we will have fun running up and down the stairs. Our room will be on the second floor."

"Are you going to have the chest in our room?" Robert asked.

"Yes, Grandfather McCormick's chest will have a special place," Cyrus said.

As the house progressed, Cyrus was even more excited. He loved the feel of wood. When the panels were in place in the rooms, he ran his fingers over the smooth hard wood.

"This is what they call wainscoting," Cyrus informed Jo and Robert. "It's the wooden lining of the wall. It's called paneling, too," he added. Cyrus liked to learn new words and he liked even better to use them. He also liked to know different words for the same things.

Cyrus was sure he had never seen anything quite as beautiful as the carved wooden mantel for the fireplace.

"Mother, this is elegant," Cyrus told her, as

he ran his fingers over the elaborately carved wood that had a high polish.

"Now that your father is a prosperous farmer," his mother said, "we can now have the kind of house I have dreamed of for years and years." She looked toward the old log house. "But I shall always have a special love for our former home." She paused. "You children were born there."

"I'm glad I was born in the log house," Cyrus said, "but I will love the new house, too."

"I'm proud of your father in so many ways," Mrs. McCormick said. "He is not only a good farmer and an inventor, but he is also an artist." She touched the mantel. "He has carved this wood so carefully."

"Papa can do anything," Cyrus said with feeling, and he meant it.

Suddenly he thought of the reaper. The reaper was about the only thing his father had ever

142

attempted that he had not finished. This house was being finished, though, and soon there would be some new furniture, too.

When his father and mother decided to go to Richmond and Lynchburg to buy furniture, Cyrus wanted to go with them. But they were making a quick trip on the stagecoach and would only be gone a few days.

"I would rather you stayed here and looked after your brothers and sisters," his mother said.

Mrs. McCormick was excited about this trip to a big city. "Robert, I know exactly what I want in mahogany and fruit wood to make the rooms of our house truly elegant."

Mr. McCormick smiled. "You have good taste, Mary Ann."

Cyrus loved to hear his mother use the word, "elegant." He liked to use it himself. Anything "elegant" was such a contrast to the plain, severe church where they prayed on Sunday. Something "elegant" was in line with his mother, who loved to put on her prettiest silk dresses to call on a neighbor.

There was one dress that Cyrus called "The Peacock." It was a rich royal blue taffeta and the braid was almost the same shade of green as the feathers in the crested peacock's tail.

Cyrus was pleased that his mother was taking this "elegant" dress with her to the big city. It made him happy to have her wear fine clothes.

Walnut Grove

THE SPINNING wheel and loom were also buzzing these days. The flax, raised on the plantation, after being harvested and dried, was made into thread on the spinning wheel and then woven into cloth on the loom.

Cyrus had always considered Walnut Grove a very busy place, but there was a great deal more activity now with the building of the new brick house.

There were all the necessary things that had to be done to keep the people on the plantation in food and clothing.

The cattle and hogs gave the year's meat

supply for the brine barrel. Then pounds of the meat went into the smokehouse. Candles were made from the tallow, and oil made soap for the household.

The hides, taken to the nearby tannery, were made into shoes and harness.

The grain was ground into flour at the grist mill on the plantation. The timber cut from the McCormick land was made into lumber at the sawmill the family had built.

The day they were felling several acres of timber, Cyrus and his father went to the woods with the cutters. Cyrus hoped they would not pick the walnut tree where he had carved his initial that day, years ago when he was five.

He looked closely at the carving. The C was not as clear as it once was. He could not believe that a tree could grow so fast. This walnut was really a big tree now.

The boy turned to his father. "Papa," he

begged, "please don't let the men cut down this walnut tree."

"It's a sturdy tree," Mr. McCormick said. "There's good lumber there. Why shouldn't we cut it down?" he asked.

"It's my tree," Cyrus said, hesitantly.

"Why is it your tree?" his father asked.

Then Cyrus told him about his trip to the woods and carving the first letter of his name and the year of his fifth birthday.

Mr. McCormick rubbed his hand over the trunk. *"C-1814,"* he said. He turned to his son. "That most certainly is your tree and we won't cut it down."

Cyrus caught a note of tenderness that was not heard too often in his father's voice when Mr. McCormick said, "Son, you are quite a boy."

As they walked back later that day, his father said, "We have an excellent location for our house. From the lawn we can look down the

slope and over the fields to the Blue Ridge Mountains. We have a beautiful place, and I hope my family will always be proud of Walnut Grove Plantation."

Cyrus certainly was proud of his home. Cyrus had been troubled for some time. He wanted to make something very special for his mother for the new house. He had thought about it often, but he could not decide what he could make well.

Then, when his father said "Walnut Grove" with so much feeling, he knew what he was going to make. On a plaque he would carve the name of the McCormick plantation.

He spent a great deal of time picking out a slab of black walnut. Then there were tedious hours of sandpapering the wood.

One day Jo found him sitting in the shade of the walnut tree. "Cyrus," he said, "you're working mighty hard on that piece of wood."

149

"It has to be very smooth," Cyrus said, not looking up. "Do you remember how much time I spent whittling that wood for the globe?"

"Yes, I do!" Jo's eyes almost popped. "Will you have to spend as much time on this?"

"No," Cyrus answered. "But it has to be as smooth as I can possibly make it."

"What are you going to do with it when it is smoothed down?" Jo asked. He was always curious and eager to know anything that absorbed his friend.

Cyrus looked up and winked. "It's a secret," he said. "When it is finished, I will tell you." Then he smiled. "By that time you will have already guessed."

"You always have a secret," Jo said, disappointed. "You make me more curious than ever. Please tell me," he begged.

Cyrus closed his mouth tightly and shook his head firmly.

150

"I give up," Jo said. "You won't tell me until you want to, and that won't be until whatever you are doing is finished."

Cyrus nodded. "That's right, Jo." He smiled and went back to smoothing the walnut with fine sandpaper.

Weeks of work went into Cyrus's secret. Many more weeks went into the building of the new brick house.

At last they moved into the big house. There sometimes seemed to be even more confusion than before.

The children said they had two houses, a big house and a little house.

Cyrus couldn't get used to so much room, but he was delighted with the beauty of the new home.

The day that almost all of the furniture was arranged to Mrs. McCormick's satisfaction, Cyrus decided to give his mother the present.

At the evening meal, Cyrus did not eat much, only his cup of milk. He was too excited.

When everyone had finished, Cyrus turned to his mother. "May I be excused?" he asked politely.

"What is your hurry?" she asked.

"It's a surprise," Cyrus said. "May I get it?"

His mother smiled and then nodded.

Cyrus jumped out of his chair and ran to the old chest where he had kept the gift all the time he was working on it.

He held the present behind him and walked slowly toward the table.

"Mother, this is for you and the new house," he said shyly as he handed it to her.

Mrs. McCormick looked at the highly polished plaque, her eyes smiling. "Walnut Grove," she read out loud.

"Robert," she said to her husband, "this is beautiful work that our son has done for us."

Mrs. McCormick studied the plaque more closely. "It must go in a very special place in our new home. Where shall we put it?"

"On the mantel in the big room," Mr. McCormick said with pride.

"That is where it should be," she replied. She got up and kissed her son on the forehead.

Cyrus, his hand holding tight to his mother's, went with her to the room with the carved mantel to hang the plaque.

A Cradle
and a Plow

IT WAS HARVEST time. Everyone at Walnut Grove Plantation, including Mrs. McCormick, was working in the fields.

The grain had ripened fast this year, which meant that from sunrise to sunset they would be in the fields cutting and raking the wheat.

"I couldn't stand such steady work 365 days in the year," Cyrus said to Jo as he paused a minute to rest. "When we are older, maybe next year, we'll be carrying one of those heavy hardwood cradles."

"I'm not going to worry about that until the time comes," Jo answered as he raked.

154

Cyrus worried more than Jo did. "I'll figure out something to make it easier for us," Cyrus said determinedly.

All through the harvest season he thought about the kind of cradle he wanted to make.

When the last bundle of wheat had been tied, Cyrus went to the barn to look at the cradles. He lifted one of them.

"Is that ever heavy!" he said out loud. He had a hard time taking it to the blacksmith shop because it was so heavy.

"These cradles weigh too much," Cyrus said. Then his eyes brightened. "That's the problem I'm going to solve!"

He knew that certain woods weighed more than others. Oak was heavy, but pine was light. He picked up different pieces of wood that were scattered about the shop.

Never before had he been quite so conscious of so many kinds of wood. He knew he must

have a durable wood because the cradles had to be strong and sturdy.

He stumbled onto a piece of locust wood. He picked it up. It was light and it seemed strong and durable. Now he knew what wood he would use for the lightweight cradle.

"Cyrus," Jo called from the yard.

"I'm here in the shop," Cyrus answered.

Jo came in breathless. "I've been looking

everywhere for you. I didn't expect to find you here in the shop this hot day."

"I have an idea," Cyrus said, whittling away at the piece of locust wood.

"You and your father are full of ideas," Jo said. "What is it this time?"

"A light cradle made of locust wood," Cyrus answered proudly. "This attachment of finger-like rods will go on the scythe. It will make it easier on us, because it will be much lighter than the other cradles."

"That sounds all right," Jo said. "Maybe we won't dread the harvest season quite so much."

"Since you approve of my idea," Cyrus said, "how about helping me?" Cyrus beckoned to Jo.

"I'll help put away the tools when we are finished," Jo said.

Cyrus blushed. "I learned my lesson the hard way. From now on I hope I can spend more time in the shop."

Cyrus had learned another lesson. He needed to spend time planning his work carefully. Cyrus worked on several ideas for improvements of the tools during the next few years.

Cyrus sat at his desk in his room at Walnut Grove Plantation. He picked up the quill pen and wrote the date, "May 12, 1831," on a sheet of white paper.

William Massie had urged him for quite some time to build him a hillside plow.

The purpose of this letter was to tell his friend Massie that he would try to build a plow for him that would work well on the steep hillsides.

After Cyrus had finished writing one page, he read the letter over carefully. Cyrus realized that he had not expressed himself clearly and that the sentences were much too long.

He crumpled the paper and tossed it into the box by the fireplace.

Cyrus picked up another sheet of paper. This

time he wrote a much shorter letter. When he had finished, he read it over and checked it carefully for spelling and punctuation.

The following month, when the plow was finished, Cyrus decided to patent it. That way he would be protected if other people should decide to copy his invention.

He was proud of the sketches he had made of this special plow. Since Washington was not too far away, he traveled to the capital and personally delivered the drawing to the government offices where patents were filed.

As he left the building, Cyrus looked back. "That was an excellent idea to patent the hillside plow in my name," he said to the trees. As he walked along the way, he smiled and looked far ahead. "This year I really believe is going to be my lucky year!" He walked faster now, anxious to get back to Rockridge County and to Walnut Grove Plantation.

Harvest 1831

EACH YEAR Cyrus was spending more time in the shop and less time in the fields. William and Leander had taken on some of his work with the crops. Robert and Susan had died in an epidemic in 1826. Cyrus missed them very much these past years.

Cyrus was now doing much of the repairing of tools and the shoeing of the horses. He took his work seriously. Many of his friends who had been in school with him years ago now had their own farms. Since Cyrus's father needed him, he stayed on at Walnut Grove.

The reaper that Mr. McCormick had tried out

in many harvests of long ago was now completely covered with dust.

Cyrus wished very much that his father would take time to work on it, especially in the winter months. Since Mr. McCormick had called it a failure, Cyrus dared not talk about the machine.

All the farmers complained about the rush at harvest time and the high cost of helpers. Virginia was one of the important wheat states of the country. But some farmers were so discouraged, they seriously considered planting crops other than grain.

A skilled worker in the field could only cut three acres a day, and new men at the job were hardly worth their wages. It didn't pay a farmer to keep slaves the year around just to use them for harvesting.

Cyrus noticed that his father was preoccupied these days. He hoped it meant that he was thinking about making some changes in the reaper.

Several times when they were both in the shop, Cyrus started to make a suggestion about the machine. His father, however, ignored him, but later Mr. McCormick started to work on the reaper again. When it was tested in the early harvest of 1831, it would not cut the wheat.

"I'll never be able to make that reaper work," Mr. McCormick said, shaking his head.

"Maybe a different knife would help," Cyrus offered.

"It's no use, Son," his father said kindly. "This is final. I'm not going to worry about this machine another day." Mr. McCormick started down the road.

Cyrus thought for a moment. Did he dare ask his father if he could try? He ran down the road after him. "Papa," he said, "would you object if I try?" he asked.

"Why waste your time?" Mr. McCormick asked, puzzled. "If it were possible to make a successful reaper, someone by now would have done it. There's a greater demand than ever for a harvesting machine."

"That's why I want to try," Cyrus said eagerly.

Mr. McCormick looked at his son, standing straight and tall before him.

Cyrus hoped with all his heart that his father would understand why he wanted to experiment with a different kind of machine.

"If God is willing, your machine may work." Mr. McCormick spoke slowly.

Cyrus was grateful for his father's faith. "I'll be busy in the shop for a long time," Cyrus said, as he turned in that direction.

Several hours later Jo found Cyrus in the shop. "What are you doing?" he asked.

"I'm about ready to make my own reaper," Cyrus said as he examined different pieces of wood. "I'll make a model first. That way I'll save time later on."

The first model did not work. The knife did not cut the way Cyrus had expected it would do. The second one was an improvement, but it had many faults.

"You puzzle me," Jo said one day. "You don't seem to be discouraged even though those funny toys you call models are not working too well."

Cyrus looked up. "Papa worked hard. I know I'm in for a long period of disappointment," he said. "I think I'm on the right track. At least I hope so."

At last, after many more models, Cyrus made one that seemed to satisfy him.

"Jo, it works!" Cyrus shouted. "See how it cuts. The horse will pull the reaper, not push the machine like Papa's did."

"Then the horse will flatten down the grain," Jo objected.

"The horse will start at the edge of the field and pull the machine," Cyrus explained, his voice eager. "Then the horse will walk on the part of the field that the reaper has already cut."

Cyrus moved the model reaper along the imaginary field. "This triangle is the divider that separates the grain that's ready to be cut. That will keep the grain from tangling. That was what always worried Papa. He never could figure out a way to keep the wheat from getting tangled."

Jo scratched his curly head. "I don't quite understand. I hope you do."

"I think I do," Cyrus said, but this time he wasn't quite so certain. "Now I'm ready to draw the pattern."

"You mean you'll draw the little machine on paper!" Jo was amazed. "You haven't time. The oats are ripening fast."

"I'll work as fast as I can," Cyrus said. "I wish I had a thousand weeks to work on my reaper."

"The harvest is almost over," Jo said, looking

out toward the golden grain that was dancing in the wind.

Cyrus made an outline of his machine on a sheet of paper. Even though his reaper was clear in his mind and he had made a model, he could not seem to scale it so that it was in balance.

He glanced down at all the crumpled sheets of paper he had used. Why couldn't he draw the reaper the way it should be? He knew that his problems would not be solved easily.

"It's the divider that's going to make all the difference in the world," he said. "The knives that cut out and in."

"You better hurry," Jo warned him, "or you will be too late this year. The sun is mighty bright these days and much of the oats are almost too ripe."

"The machine is still not the way it should be," Cyrus said, working harder than ever on the pattern.

"Your mom's mighty worried," Jo said sympathetically. "She says you don't eat enough to keep a bird alive, and you are working round the clock."

"It takes time to eat, and I haven't any time to waste," Cyrus answered impatiently. "I don't work on Sunday for I'm attending church most of that day."

"You might get sick, and then you would be in a bad fix," Jo insisted.

"I can't get sick." Cyrus sighed wearily. "Maybe I better eat, just to be sure." He reached for some bread and cold beef Hannah had brought a few hours earlier. "It tastes good," Cyrus said. "I'll be able to work better than ever." He smiled at Jo. "Maybe I'll be able to think better, too."

"I'm going to tell your mother that you licked the platter clean!" Jo said as he hurried out the door and down the path.

Cyrus laughed as he started once again on the problem of making his reaper work.

Mr. Steele, the McCormick's neighbor, was as interested in Cyrus's experiment as all the other people in that area were.

Mr. Steele came into the shop one morning. "Cyrus," he said, "I have a small field of oats I'm saving for you to cut."

"That's what I need, Mr. Steele," Cyrus said. He looked up from the wheel that he was working on. "I have to have some ripe grain to test this machine. Thank you."

"When will it be ready to cut my grain?" Mr. Steele asked.

"I hope to be ready in a day or two," Cyrus answered. "Right now I'm not so certain. I'm having a lot of trouble."

"Good luck," Mr. Steele said as he walked out of the shop.

Now Cyrus worked even harder than ever. He

knew Mr. Steele's oats might be too ripe in a few days.

"I'm ready to test my reaper," Cyrus announced to his father several days later. They were both in the shop. "I'll test it in a small patch of grain," he explained.

The whole family came out to watch the reaper work. His brother William, now sixteen, was excited. So were John, now twelve, and Leander, a year younger, and Amanda.

The knife clicked as the reaper moved slowly. Cyrus rode Doll, who didn't seem to mind the noise as she pulled the machine. Jo raked the stalks off the platform, as the knife cut them.

The reaper hit a big rock. Cyrus jumped down from his horse and checked to see that nothing had been broken. He motioned for Doll to go on ahead, and the reaper cut again.

One row of wheat had been cut. Now Cyrus was ready to make a turn to start the second row.

Jo had been so busy raking the grain that it was all helter-skelter. The cut grain was in the way of the reaper. William gathered it up so the horse could get through.

At least the machine was cutting, but Cyrus knew now it needed a different kind of knife, maybe one with a saw-toothed edge.

Even Cyrus could not believe that the grain patch was almost cut. It had been done in such a short time compared to the time it would have taken men with cradles to harvest the same amount of grain.

"Your machine really does a trim job of cutting," Mr. McCormick said proudly.

"It could be better," Cyrus answered, but he was pleased that his reaper had cut as well as it had. "I'm sure the knife should have a rough edge. Our neighbor down the road a few miles can make a saw-toothed knife, I'm sure, from the pattern."

170

Cyrus was glad that he had sketched every part of the machine. It had been tedious and discouraging. Now that he was really racing for time, he was relieved that the sketch was finished. All he would have to do was to give the neighbor the pattern. Surely, if John McCown understood that he needed the knife in a hurry, he would make it as soon as he could.

Then the reaper would be ready to take over to John Steele's farm.

Cyrus was quite sure now that he had discovered a practical cutting principle. The blacksmith, John McCown, had followed instructions well and Cyrus liked the new blade that had teeth like a saw.

But he still had other problems. There had to be a better way to have the cut grain ready for binding. So he changed the divider and the reel, too.

When you looked at the reaper, the most striking part about it was the reel that resembled a windmill or big paddlewheel.

This reel had wooden arms carrying horizontal slats that rotated by gear and pulley. The reel pressed backward, holding the stalks of grain in position for the knife to cut.

The knife in the grain cradle went back and forth across the grain, cutting the stalks. Since the knife could not push the stalks down, Cyrus had made fingers of wood, set two or three inches apart, that held the stalks firmly in front of the knife.

The fingers were steady, but the knife moved back and forth. It was like a cradle swinging. Then the cut-off stalks fell onto the platform. Jo would rake them off the platform and then the grain would be ready to be put into bundles.

Cyrus again rechecked the principal parts of the reaper. There were seven main parts in this first reaper—the divider, the reel, the knife that went back and forth, the fingers or guards, the platform, the main wheel and gearing, and the front-side draft traction.

"It's ready now," Cyrus shouted at last. He was excited.

Old Charlie Anderson, Jo's father, and Anthony, Negro helpers at Walnut Grove Plantation, started down the road with the reaper.

"Steady those horses," Cyrus warned them. "The rattle of the reaper and the flapping canvas may make them nervous."

Cyrus hurried into the house to change into a clean broadcloth suit. Soon he mounted Peacock and headed toward Mr. Steele's place.

As he caught up with the reaper, he heard the reel clicking as it went round and round. The canvas in the divider flapped in the wind.

There was something wonderful about this July day, 1831. This was his day, the day he and his father had been waiting for for years.

To the east was the Blue Ridge, with the morning sun. Away in the distance were the Alleghenies, and beyond hundreds of acres of land that someday would be planted in grain, if his machine could pass this second test.

Cyrus was pleased that his family wanted to watch this second field test. But he had not expected all these other people.

Cyrus heard one of the neighbors say, "It's a right smart curious sort of thing, but I can't believe that it will come to much."

The remark did not bother Cyrus. This was his day. He knew that at last he had made a reaper that would help the farmers.

"Are you ready?" Cyrus shouted to Anthony who was riding the horse.

"Yes, sir," Anthony answered.

Jo was standing by the reaper, rake in hand. "I'm ready for the machine to start," he said.

Cyrus stood behind the reaper.

174

"Giddap," Anthony called. Doll strained a bit and the machine moved. The reel turned, sweeping forward and downward. It caught the tall stalks and held them in front of the knife. The saw-toothed blade moved back and forth, cutting the oats. Then the reel turned backward, pushing the grain onto the platform. Jo raked the oats off onto the ground.

Cyrus walked close behind. His machine was cutting the grain. That was what counted. One acre, two acres, then six acres!

Mr. Steele walked quickly over to Cyrus. "Your reaper has cut the six acres of oats in record time." He took off his hat. "Four men working steadily for half a day with the cradles could not have done as well."

"Son, this time your machine really works," Mr. McCormick said. He patted Cyrus's strong shoulder.

"I'm going to make the fingers of iron instead

176

of wood, and I'll arrange the platform so that it can be adjusted to the heights of the knife," Cyrus said.

"Knowing you, Son," Mr. McCormick smiled, "you'll make many changes before you patent it. You're a young man. You have many years ahead to perfect this machine that means so much to our family. Someday I hope it will carry our name. The McCormick reaper sounds mighty good!"

"I don't mind experimenting more, Papa, if it makes for a better reaper," Cyrus replied. "Since we live in Virginia, don't you think that the name Virginia reaper would have more weight with farmers than our family name would have?"

Mr. McCormick thought a moment. "Perhaps it would," he said. "This Virginia reaper will change the farmer's way of life, Son," he added proudly. "You are truly the farmer's friend!"

Reaper for
the World

DURING THE NEXT few years Cyrus spent much of his time selling hempbrakes in Kentucky. The hempbrake was a new tool which his father had made for harvesting hemp or flax.

Frequently young Cyrus talked with people about his Virginia reaper. He had had little time to make any changes in the reaper since he had first tested it in 1831.

Cyrus, who now was twenty-two years old, often thought, "My reaper has already helped the farmer, but I can make it better. I can change it so that it will make harvesting even easier than it is now for the farmers."

It was then that Cyrus decided to spend every moment that he could spare toward making his reaper a better machine. He would return home.

One day in the spring of 1834, Cyrus left Lexington, Virginia, to ride Peacock the last few miles to Walnut Grove Plantation. In his saddlebag, he carried a copy of the April issue of *Mechanics' Magazine*.

Cryus looked forward to living at home again. Maybe he and his father would find time to play their fiddles together.

When Cyrus reached home, Mary Caroline was looking out of the window. "Cyrus is home," she called to her sister Amanda and her brothers. The boys, William, John, and Leander, hurried out to the barn to greet him.

Later that evening, Cyrus suddenly remembered the magazine in his saddlebag. He went out to the barn to get it.

"Listen to this, Papa," said Cyrus. He turned

to one of the stories in the magazine. "Some man by the name of Obed Hussey has made a reaper. He even has a patent on it!"

"Are you sure it's a reaper and not some other kind of machine that he has patented?" Mr. Mc-Cormick asked Cyrus.

"That's what this story says," answered Cyrus. "There are pictures of his machine, too. He even has the reaper for sale."

"You had better get our reaper patented as soon as possible," his father warned.

Mrs. McCormick said, "Cyrus, please be sure to patent the machine right away."

"I will," answered Cyrus. "I will do it tomorrow. I never once thought that someone outside our own family might build a reaper, too. However, these pictures of Mr. Hussey's machine prove that someone else did."

The next day, May 20, 1834, Cyrus sat down at his desk and wrote a letter to the editor of

Mechanics' Magazine. He hoped that by writing this letter, the editor would print a story about his reaper, too.

"In July, 1831," Cyrus wrote, "I tested my new reaper on the farm of Mr. Steele, our neighbor. With the help of my family and neighbors, I cut a field of wheat and then a field of oats. For the first time, wheat and oats were harvested by machine. For the first time, a farmer did not have to swing a scythe in order to cut his grain.

"Many people saw these tests. Any one of them could tell you about my reaper."

Cyrus wrote another letter that day. He wrote to the United States Patent Office in Washington, D. C. He described his new reaper and asked that a patent be sent to him. At the same time he mailed a thirty-dollar patent fee to the Treasury of the United States.

On June 21, 1834, Cyrus received a fourteen-year patent on his Virginia reaper.

It was a joyful day in the McCormick household when Cyrus announced to his parents, and his sisters and brothers, that he now had a patent for his Virginia reaper.

"I have just received this notice signed by the President of the United States," said Cyrus. "Look here," he exclaimed. "This is Andrew Jackson's name in his very own handwriting."

"Now we know this reaper is really yours for sure," Jo said happily.

"That's right, Jo," replied Cyrus.

"I think we should start making reapers for the farmers," Leander suggested.

"It cost a lot of money to build machines," Cyrus told him. "We don't have enough money to do that right now."

Cyrus looked carefully at the important paper that had come from the United States capital. "This notice says that I am the only person allowed the right to make, build, use, or sell the reaper in our country," he said. "Isn't that wonderful, Papa?"

"That sounds as if everything is in your favor," Mr. McCormick replied.

"I don't know, Father," said Cyrus. "A man named Obed Hussey has made a reaper, and perhaps other people in the country also have tried to build reaping machines. If they have, we may face many problems."

"When there is great need for something," Mr. McCormick replied, "many people try to fill that need. Not everyone succeeds. Some people fail, just as I failed. Someone else, perhaps you, Cyrus, will be successful."

"Papa," Cyrus answered quickly, "I owe everything to you. I found a way to make my reaper work because you already had made many tests."

Mr. McCormick sighed, "Son, I fear that your problems are just beginning. You will need much money to make and sell reapers."

"If we work very hard on the farm and save our money," said Cyrus, "we will be able to begin making reapers soon."

Cyrus hoped to make money in a new business, an iron works, that he was starting. However, his plans were unsuccessful. It was not until the year 1840 that he sold his first reapers.

That same year two men came to Walnut Grove especially to see Cyrus.

"Good day, gentlemen," greeted Cyrus. "I am Cyrus McCormick. What may I do for you?"

The two men introduced themselves. One of them said, "We come from the James River Valley some miles to the north. We want to buy two of your reapers, Mr. McCormick."

"I don't know that part of Virginia," Cyrus answered regretfully. "I am sorry to say that I haven't any reapers for sale either."

"We want you to make two reapers for us just like the one you have," the other man insisted.

184

"Are you men neighbors?" asked Cyrus.

The two men nodded.

"Then I have a plan," said Cyrus. "Why don't you buy one reaper and share it?"

The visitors looked at each other and smiled.

Cyrus went on, "That way it won't cost either of you too much. You can pay part of the cost now. Then you can give me the rest of the money a little at a time. What do you think of this plan?"

Both of the men agreed that Cyrus's suggestion was a wonderful idea. In the years to follow, this idea became very popular with farmers.

Cyrus's new plan was a big help to the farmer. It meant that a farmer would not have to wait until he had saved all the money he needed to buy a reaper. He could use the machine to harvest his grain. Then he could pay a little money on the machine each time he sold some of the harvested grain.

In 1842, Cyrus set the price of the reaper at

one hundred dollars. That same year he sold seven reapers. By 1844, he had sold fifty machines.

Cyrus and his brother Leander were now in business together. They had several men working for them. These men were showing the reaper to people in many of the eastern and southern parts of the United States.

For ten years, beginning in 1840, Cyrus spent most of his time traveling. He made many friends. He was busy arranging tests of his reaper for the people in the farming sections of the East and South. Different newspapers printed kind words about Cyrus and the reaper. This pleased him very much.

As the years went by, Cyrus realized that Virginia was not in the center of the grain-growing region. He began to think of moving his business.

Cyrus felt his business should be nearer big lakes and rivers. Then the reapers could be shipped more easily to the West. It was in the

West that more and more people each year were farming hundreds of acres of grain. Cyrus decided that he must leave Virginia.

By 1847, a brick building in Chicago, Illinois, carried the McCormick name over the door.

One morning when he entered his office, Cyrus noticed an interesting envelope in his mail. There were colorful foreign stamps on it. Inside the envelope there was a letter telling about the first great World's Fair which was to be held in London, England, in 1851.

Deep in thought, Cyrus stroked his heavy beard. He walked from his desk to the window. He studied the people on the sidewalk below.

Cyrus's factory was now four years old. Moving to Chicago had been wise. Farmers in the West were eager to learn all about his reaper.

Chicago was little more than a village when Cyrus arrived. However, he had felt that the city would one day be the gateway to the West.

Cyrus smiled. "I was right," he thought. "Chicago is growing very fast. My company is making more and more reapers every year."

His thoughts drifted back twenty years. He had traveled to Washington, D. C., to patent his hillside plow. The Virginia reaper had passed the field test at Mr. Steele's farm. Cyrus had wanted to make several additional improvements on the invention. He had delayed filling out the papers for a patent on the reaper.

"What a mistake that was," he thought. "There have been many lawsuits. I fear that there will be many more."

He walked back to his desk. He picked up the letter that had come to him across the Atlantic Ocean from London.

Years ago, when he was making the globe, he had told Jo, "I'm going to see the world!"

"At last my chance has come," he thought. "I'll go to England to show my reaper at the fair."

By this time the reaper was well known in the United States. Cyrus thought it was now time to show the machine to the farmers in Europe. His eyes danced with excitement.

Later that year, in September of 1851, Cyrus read an article about the reaper in the *London Times*. The writer was very excited about the American machine. He wrote, "If the McCormick reaper fulfills its promise, it will be worth the cost of the whole exhibition!"

Cyrus's reaper won the famous Council Medal at the London World's Fair.

A very special kind of happiness came to Cyrus in 1858. On January 26 of that year he was married to Nancy Fowler.

Mrs. McCormick was greatly interested in her husband's business. She was very helpful to Cyrus in many ways. His sons and daughters were a special joy to him.

When the Civil War broke out in 1861, the

nearly 50,000 reapers then in use released thousands of men for duty with the army. The use of these reapers made it possible for large quantities of grain to be harvested. Much of this grain was shipped to Europe. The income from this trade helped to relieve the great financial strain on the United States Government due to the burdens of the war.

A great fire occurred in Chicago in the fall of 1871. The McCormick factory burned to the ground along with thousands of other buildings.

The man who kept the company's records was upset. "All our books and records were burned in the fire," he said. "What shall we do?" He and Cyrus were standing on the blackened ground where, only the day before, workmen had been busy making reapers.

"The farmers are our good friends," Cyrus replied confidently. "We will write to tell them about what has happened to our factory. We will explain that all our records were burned. I am sure they will make their payments on time."

Cyrus was right. He had an unusual ability to inspire loyalty. The people who worked for him were loyal, and the farmers who used his reapers were loyal, too.

For nearly thirty-five years, Cyrus continued to win major prizes for his reaper at world's fairs in Paris, London, Hamburg, Vienna, Philadelphia, and Melbourne.

The French especially approved of Cyrus's services. He was made a chevalier and later an officer in the Legion of Honor.

In 1879, at the age of seventy, Cyrus was elected a member of the French Academy of Sciences. He was honored for "having done more for agriculture than any other living man."

Cyrus McCormick's long desire had come true. He was a friend to the farmers of the world!

More About This Book

WHEN CYRUS HALL McCORMICK LIVED

1809   CYRUS HALL McCORMICK WAS BORN IN VIRGINIA, FEBRUARY 15.

There were seventeen states in the Union.

James Madison was President.

The population of the country was about 7,046,000.

1809–1822   CYRUS LIVED AT WALNUT GROVE PLANTATION AND ATTENDED FIELD SCHOOL.

The War of 1812 was fought, 1812-1815.

"The Star-Spangled Banner" was written, 1814.

Florida was purchased from Spain, 1819.

The first steamship crossed the Atlantic, 1819.

1822–1830   CYRUS STUDIED WITH A TUTOR AND CONTINUED TO WORK WITH HIS FATHER.

The Monroe Doctrine was issued, 1823.

The Erie Canal was completed, 1825.

Peter Cooper built the first steam locomotive in the United States, 1830.

1831 CYRUS SUCCESSFULLY HARVESTED GRAIN WITH
HIS NEW MODEL OF THE REAPER.

Samuel Morse invented the telegraph, 1835.

American settlers reached Oregon, 1836.

1840 CYRUS MADE THE FIRST REAPER TO SELL TO HIS
NEIGHBORING FARMERS.

The Mexican War was fought, 1846-1848.

Elias Howe invented the sewing machine, 1846.

Gold was discovered in California, 1848.

1851 CYRUS DISPLAYED THE REAPER AT THE FIRST
WORLD'S FAIR IN LONDON, ENGLAND.

The War between the States was fought, 1861-
1865.

The first transcontinental railroad was completed, 1869.

Alexander G. Bell invented the telephone, 1876.

1879 CYRUS WAS ELECTED A MEMBER OF THE FRENCH
ACADEMY OF SCIENCES.

Thomas Edison invented the electric light bulb,
1879.

Clara Barton founded the American Red Cross,
1881.

The Civil Service System was begun, 1883.

194

1884 CYRUS HALL McCORMICK DIED, MAY 13.

There were thirty-eight states in the Union.

Chester A. Arthur was President.

The population of the country was about
55,272,000.

DO YOU REMEMBER?

1. When and where was Cyrus Hall McCormick born?

2. Who was Cyrus McCormick's devoted playmate?

3. Why did Cyrus name his horse Peacock?

4. What unfinished machine sat in the corner of Mr.
   McCormick's blacksmith shop?

5. Why was the field trial in 1816 of Mr. McCormick's
   reaper unsuccessful?

6. Why did Mr. McCormick not allow Cyrus to keep
   the knife he had received in a trade?

7. Why did the entire family look forward to the visit
   of the Yankee Peddler?

8. How did Cyrus learn that younger brothers may
   sometimes be helpful as well as annoying?

9. What were some of the experiences Cyrus shared
   with his Grandfather McCormick?

10. Why did Cyrus make a globe for his class at the Field School?

11. Why did Cyrus and Jo prefer to practice their music away from the house?

12. What materials for the new house were produced on Walnut Grove Plantation?

13. What improvement did Cyrus make in the cradle?

14. When did Mr. McCormick give up his experimenting and turn the work on the reaper over to Cyrus?

15. Why was there such a long delay before reapers were made for other farmers?

16. What did the people of England think of the reaper?

IT'S FUN TO LOOK UP THESE THINGS

1. Why was a hammer with a hickory handle better than some other hammers to Mr. McCormick?

2. With whom was the country fighting in the War of 1812?

3. What made an agate seem more important to a marble shooter than other marbles?

4. What stories of the bluebird as a good luck symbol can you find?

196

5. What is the study of surveying?

6. How did the studying of surveying and mathematics help Cyrus in his adult life?

7. What sort of party was held at a cornhusking?

8. What were some of the many philanthropic actions of Cyrus McCormick as an adult?

INTERESTING THINGS YOU CAN DO

1. Make a list of the inventions to improve transportation, communication, and working conditions made during Cyrus McCormick's lifetime. Prepare a scrapbook showing the old and the new devices.

2. Gather information on when and where World's Fairs have been held since the first in London, 1851. Describe the plans which are being made for the next World's Fair.

3. Make a model of the Walnut Grove Plantation and include the different parts of the plantation which contributed to the everyday needs of the people living there.

4. Plan an imaginary trip to all the historical places which have been set aside to commemorate the achievements of Cyrus Hall McCormick.

OTHER BOOKS YOU MAY ENJOY READING

Aleck Bell: Ingenious Boy, Mabel Cleland Widdemer. Trade and School Editions, Bobbs-Merrill.

First Transcontinental Railroad, The, Adele Nathan. Trade Edition, Random House. School Edition, Hale.

Eli Whitney: Boy Mechanic, Dorothea Snow. Trade and School Editions, Bobbs-Merrill.

Everyday Machines and How They Work, Herman Schneider and Jeanne Bendick, Whittlesey House.

Samuel Morse: Inquisitive Boy, Dorothea Snow. Trade and School Editions, Bobbs-Merrill.

Tom Edison: Boy Inventor, Sue Guthridge. Trade and School Editions, Bobbs-Merrill.

INTERESTING WORDS IN THIS BOOK

agate (ăg′ĭt) : kind of stone with colors in stripes and cloudy patches

bellows (bĕl′ōz) : instrument used to make a current of air for blowing fires

broadcloth (brôd′klôth′) : fine grade of woolen cloth

camphor (kăm′fēr) : whitish crystaline gum with very strong odor used in medicines and moth balls

compass (kŭm′pås) : instrument for drawing circles, transferring measurements, dividing areas consisting of two upright rods joined together at top by a hinge

confidence (kŏn′fĭ dĕns) : boldness; having trust

continent (kŏn′tĭ nĕnt) : one of the large divisions of land on the earth

cradle (krā′d′l) : frame of wood fastened to a scythe in a fingerlike arrangement to use in harvest

creative (krė ā′tĭv) : having power to make something which is new plan or design

elaborately (ė lăb′ȯ rĭt lĭ) : worked out with great care and detailed plan

exaggerating (ĕg zăj′ēr āt′ĭng) : enlarging beyond truth or reason

experiment (ĕks pēr′ĭ mĕnt) : trial made to discover something unknown or to prove an idea

gutter (gŭt′ēr) : narrow channel worn by running water

grist mill (grĭst mĭll) : mill for grinding grain

hearth (härth) : bottom of fireplace or forge on which the fire is made

helter-skelter (hĕl′tēr- skĕl′tēr) : in disorder

impatient (ĭm pā′shĕnt) : restlessly eager

kiln (kĭl; kĭln) : large stove or furnace for hardening, burning, or drying anything

loom (lo͞om) : frame for weaving cloth

mimic (mĭm′ĭk) : copy closely the actions of another

mincing (mĭns′ĭng) : walking with short steps

niche (nĭch) : position especially suitable for something or someone

plaque (plăk) : flat, thin piece of metal or wood upon which a design is carved or painted

resourceful (rė̇ sōrs′fo͝ol) : able to meet unusual situations or needs

responsibility (rė̇ spŏn′ sĭ bĭl′ĭ tĭ) : ability to meet duties or obligations

sentimental (sĕn′tĭ mĕn′tăl) : easily affected by one's feelings

sickle (sĭk′l) : hand tool consisting of a curved steel blade fitted into a short handle

tallow (tăl′ō) : fat of cattle and sheep, used in candles, soap, and margarine

tannery (tăn′ẽr ĭ) : place where skins are made into leather

tedious (tē′dĭ ŭs) : tiresome, boring

wainscoting (wān′skŭt ĭng) : lower three or four feet of wall finished differently from the remainder

Childhood

OF FAMOUS AMERICANS

ATHLETES

BE RUTH, *Van Riper*
THORPE, *Van Riper*
UTE ROCKNE, *Van Riper*
GEHRIG, *Van Riper*

UTHORS and OMPOSERS

IE PYLE, *Wilson*
RRIET BEECHER STOWE, *Widdemer*
ES WHITCOMB RILEY, *Mitchell*
ES FENIMORE COOPER, *Winders*
N PHILIP SOUSA, *Weil*
TE DOUGLAS WIGGIN, *Mason*
ISA ALCOTT, *Wagoner*
RK TWAIN, *Mason*
RY MAPES DODGE, *Mason*
PHEN FOSTER, *Higgins*
SHINGTON IRVING, *Widdemer*

BUSINESSMEN

P. GIANNINI, *Hammontree*
N WANAMAKER, *Burt*

EARLY SETTLERS

ES OGLETHORPE, *Parks*
ES STANDISH, *Stevenson*
ER STUYVESANT, *Widdemer*
GINIA DARE, *Stevenson*
LLIAM BRADFORD, *Smith*
LLIAM PENN, *Mason*

ENTERTAINERS

ANNIE OAKLEY, *Wilson*
LOTTA CRABTREE, *Place*
THE RINGLING BROTHERS, *Burt*
WILL ROGERS, *Van Riper*

EXPLORERS and PIONEERS

AMELIA EARHART, *Howe*
BUFFALO BILL, *Stevenson*
DANIEL BOONE, *Stevenson*
DAVY CROCKETT, *Parks*
GEORGE ROGERS CLARK, *Wilkie*
JED SMITH, *Burt*
JIM BOWIE, *Winders*
JIM BRIDGER, *Winders*
JOHN SEVIER, *Steele*
KIT CARSON, *Stevenson*
MERIWETHER LEWIS, *Bebenroth*
NARCISSA WHITMAN, *Warner*
RICHARD BYRD, *Van Riper*
ROBERT PEARY, *Clark*
WILL CLARK, *Wilkie*
ZEB PIKE, *Stevenson*

FOUNDERS of OUR NATION

ALEC HAMILTON, *Higgins*
BEN FRANKLIN, *Stevenson*
GEORGE WASHINGTON, *Stevenson*
JOHN QUINCY ADAMS, *Weil*
NATHAN HALE, *Stevenson*
PAUL REVERE, *Stevenson*
TOM JEFFERSON, *Monsell*